BIOLOGICAL BASIS OF PHYSICAL EDUCATION

BIOLOGICAL BASIS OF PHYSICAL EDUCATION

Editor
Shamshad Ahmed

ISHA

ISHA BOOKS
Delhi-110033

Biological Basis of Physical Education

ISBN : 81-8205-241-6

Published in 2007 in India by
Isha Books,
B-63, Ist Floor, New Gupta Colony,
Near DDA Market, Delhi-110 009
Phone : 9212142040
Email : ishabooks@hotmail.com

Laser Typesetting at : Global Printers, New Delhi

Printed at :
Rajdhani Printers, Delhi

Contents

1

Meaning of Growth and Development

Individuals follow a predictable pattern of physical growth but the rate at which children and youth go through this growth varies by individual.

— During the childhood phase, children (on average) grow about 2.5 in./yr. and gain about 5 pounds/year.

— Peak height velocity of growth occurs during puberty/adolescence.

— Athletes of the same chronological age can vary by as much as 5 biological years, especially during adolescence. Therefore, with two 11-year-old swimmers, one may be 10 and the other 15, biologically. Talk about competing on uneven playing fields!

Educate athletes regarding growth cycles and factor in training program the variations in the timing of physical growth. Also, to ensure young athletes are growing properly, record basic growth data before, during, and after the season. Performance can be influenced by maturity, which is out of the athlete's control. Some young athletes, therefore, have a performance advantage over others.

— Initially, early maturers have a physical size advantage and often perform better than late maturers. These individuals experience more early success due to a physical growth advantage and not necessarily enhanced skills or abilities.

- Conversely, late maturers experience failure and frustration because they are physically "behind" their same-age (chronological) peers.
- Adolescent awkwardness due to rapid physical growth affects performance, especially for early maturers.
- Late maturers often catch up to or exceed the performance of early maturers by the mid-teen years, but only if they have stayed with the sport. Some drop out because of a lack of early performance success or, worse, are cut from the team.
- Tracking of "outstanding" kids in elementary school found that only 25% were still outstanding in later years, suggesting that early success does not predict later success.

Help early maturers keep success in perspective as late maturers will often catch up with them in terms of performance and success will be harder to achieve One means of doing this is to have early maturers compete at times, against athletes with the same abilities regardless of age. Additionally, take active steps to keep late maturers involved as they often leave the sport because of low perceptions of competence due to little early success. Be creative in helping them experience some success. Gender differences in physical growth and in the timing of the growth spurt contribute to the overall difference in the height and body shapes of females and males.

- Girls reach peak height velocity (growth spurt) between the ages of 11-13 and boys between the ages of 13-15.
- Hormonal differences in males and females cause body composition changes in adolescence, changes which are out of the athlete's control but which may impact performance (positively and negatively).
- Because males are in childhood growth longer and have a more intense growth spurt at puberty, adult males generally have a greater percentage of their height in their legs.

Males and females differ in the growth and development process; both when the growth spurt occurs and ensuing physical changes. It is important to take these differences into account when training adolescent males and females as well as to educate them on the developmental process. Because of the numerous and sometimes drastic changes, it is crucial to allow time for young athletes to get comfortable (physically and emotionally) with their changed bodies. Additionally, adaptation to the growth changes lags behind so expect it to take some time for the athlete to be able to take advantage of changes.

A Physiological Perspective

It is important for coaches to have an understanding of the biological/physiological development of the young athlete as this knowledge can and should be implemented to maximize the child's potential. There are three primary physiological performance components that undergo quantitative changes (increased size or capacity) and qualitative changes (increased efficiency) with growth and development. The components include aerobic capacity, anaerobic capacity, and muscular strength, power and endurance.

Aerobic Capacity

— V02max, the ability to take in, transport, and utilize oxygen, is the common parameter used to measure aerobic capacity.

— V02max shows significant growth from 11-13 years for females and 12-14 for males. This time frame, when significant growth can occur (sensitive period), should be maximized in the training program to develop the athlete's long term potential. The athlete is able to rapidly increase workload during this sensitive period.

— Pre-pubescent athletes show significant improvements in long duration, low intensity events and are able to enhance the utilization of their aerobic capacity.

Coaches should optimize aerobic training during this "sensitive period" (11-13 years for females/12-14 years for males) to maximize athlete's aerobic development. It is suggested that pre-pubescent athletes (ages 9-12/14) focus on longer distances (i.e., longer repeats and longer competitive events) for reasons related to both skill development and aerobic capacity development.

Anaerobic Capacity

— Anaerobic training involves high intensity, brief activities (repeats on long rest or 25yd. sprints or less).

— It has been found that high volume pre-pubescent anaerobic work results in insignificant long-term anaerobic improvement for young athletes (10-13 years). It may result in short-term time drops.

— However, higher aerobic work during this time results in increased performance across all distances not just longer distances.

— Increased anaerobic load early leads to potential maladaptation in young athletes...it is said to "tax their tank" and their ability to adapt.

— A gradual increase in the proportion of anaerobic work beginning at ages 12-14 for girls and 13-15 for boys maximizes development and enhances performance, BUT only if preceded by ample aerobic work.

Coaches need to first develop the athlete's aerobic capacity and then gradually increase anaerobic load for maximum development of anaerobic capacity.

Muscular strength, power and endurance

— A frequently asked question is whether young athletes should be strength training. It is suggested that you can see muscular gains and adaptations but only if strength training is done under the right scenario — with close supervision to ensure proper technique.

- Prior to puberty, the gains come from neuromuscular changes not changes in muscle size. With increases in steroid hormones (puberty), we see gains due to changes in muscle size (predominantly in males).

- As muscle size increases, so does strength. But, typically there is a year lag time between size/mass increases and maximum effects of strength gains in young athletes.

- Additionally, the translation of land-based strength, power, and endurance to pool performance can vary from half a year up to two years.

- The age of 14-15 is when peak gains occur; quantitative muscular changes can occur with proper training - "window of time where they are plastic". However, it is not until half a year up to two years later that this will be translated into an increase in strength.

Young athletes are not miniature adults. Because of hormonal and biological differences between children and adults, children will not increase muscle size through strength training. However, neuromuscular adaptations can occur. It is only after puberty that muscle growth occurs. Keep in mind that the ability to translate muscular work to swimming velocity is the key, as our concern is helping children swim faster. Therefore, we must ensure that strength training is implemented or modified to meet this objective.

Developmental Information

Sport performance is determined by a myriad of variables. Two athletes may be the same age but not of the same ability due to intrinsic, developmental differences in: flexibility, balance and coordination, reaction time, body composition, motivation, endurance, and self-esteem, to name a few.

Growth and development

- Growth does not occur at a continuous rate but rather is greatest at puberty.

— Growth is sequential with long bone growth occurring initially, followed by growth of the trunk, and lastly increases in muscle mass.

— Psychomotor skills (development of motor skills) cannot be integrated appropriately by the central nervous system (CNS) until age six-eight.

— Significant increases in muscle mass cannot occur in the absence of significant Levels of androgenic hormones; therefore, prior to puberty young athletes will not have significant gains in muscle mass regardless of the work they are doing.

— There are gender differences based on maturation. The ranges given are to be used as general guidelines.

Early childhood (2-5 years)

— From four-six years there is a paradoxical drop in postural and balance skills due to the young athlete being overloaded with proprioceptive (information regarding muscular dynamics and limb movement) and vestibular signals to integrate into balance control — the athlete is initially overwhelmed.

— Total attention to balance may delay improvement if other variables are present.

— Young children have very short attention spans; can only focus on one thing for a short period of time. Instruction is best offered by show and tell.

— At this age, unstructured play is important - emphasize play, exploration, fun.

— The child does not have fully mature visual skills - imprecise eye movement, relative farsightedness, lack of visual maturity which relates to a lack of coordination.

— Sport modification is necessary (i.e., T-ball).

— There seems to be no long term advantage from practicing at this age.

Childhood (6-9 years)

— Postural and balance skills mature and become automatic by about seven. Athletes demonstrate improved fundamental skills - coordinated breathing in freestyle - and most master skills to progress on to transitional skills for organized sports.

— Young athletes still have a short attention span. Additionally, they have difficulty with integration - limited memory strategies impairs rapid decision making of complex sport skills. It is still best to provide both visual and verbal instructions.

— There is conflicting results regarding the benefits of participation in terms of being more skilled as an adult if the child starts the sport now.

— The eye is a mature spheroid shape. The young athlete has better eye movement and tracking, but CNS processing lags behind so they may judge velocity well but not direction. Because of eye changes, judging the wall moving towards them may make it difficult for swimmers to learn efficient turns until vision is more completely mature.

— Sports or activities with many variables, complex skills, and rapid decision making may still be too difficult for some athletes.

Preadolescence (10-12 years)

— In terms of motor skill development, at this age there is improvement in fundamental, transitional, and postural skills.

Adolescence (13-16 years)

— Athletes are able to use memory strategies necessary for complex skills and are also able to integrate information from many sources.

— Athletes are able to focus appropriately, use selective attention, and they demonstrate advances in decision making capabilities.

— There are striking developmental differences around age 13-15 due to maturational differences.

— There may be some deterioration in postural control during peak height velocity as the athlete struggles to adjust to his/her rapidly changing body.

— "Clumsy teenager" - temporary stage requiring adjustments in interpretation of proprioceptive components for participation.

— Remember: epiphysial (growth) plate injury is most vulnerable to injury during the period of most growth.

Strength development

— As the coach, you must consider the athlete's age, level of development, maturity, desire, and level of sport skill, and also assess the risks and benefits of strength training in determining if it is appropriate for athletes.

— Girls demonstrate faster increases in the sensitive period for strength which is from 13-15 years. This is after their Peak Height Velocity time (11-13 years).

— Boys tend to evidence strength gains (14-16 yr) one year after peak height velocity (13-15 yr).

— Various mechanism by which strength gains occur:

— Motor learning

— Improvements in motor coordination

— Morphoiogical and neurological (nervous system) adaptations

Considerations in Training

— *Heat tolerance*: younger athletes are not as tolerant of excessive heat. They generate more heat, sweat less, have slower acclimatization, and get more thermal impairment with dehydration.

— *Flexibility*: found to decrease with puberty in males while some improvement is seen in females.

A Sociological Approach

The athletes you coach do not participate in sports in a vacuum. They are greatly affected and influenced by the social and cultural environment in which they live and by the social development challenges they face during child-hood and adolescence. To enhance your effectiveness in working with young athletes, it is important to take into account this social development as it impacts areas such as the athletes' goals, behaviors, needs, and self-concept. Sport sociologists attempt to understand the relationship between social development and sport participation. They assume that the achievement of maturity- and an adult sense of responsibility depend on the completion of important developmentaL tasks during childhood and adolescence.

Coaches should be aware of how the social relationships associated with sport participation are involved in the completion of these developmentaL tasks. For example: Children (7-10 years old) face the challenge of learning how to get along with peers and how to deal with authority figures apart from their parents. During these years it is important for children to learn how to stand up for themselves among their peers while at the same time understanding that their peers are different than they are. They must learn how to compromise for the sake of getting along, and how to cooperate and compete with their equals. If these social interaction skills are not learned, children may face difficulties when addressing developmental challenges during preadolescence and adolescence.

As a youth coach it is important to recognize that seven-ten year olds are expressive, spontaneous, and egocentric. You should give them room to express themselves while at the same time establishing clear-cut norms about honesty and playing by the rules. As they seek to get their way you should understand that children during this stage are only beginning to develop the ability to see the world from the perspective of others. Because these children are in the process of learning acceptable means of achieving goals, coaches should take care to make clearly explained distinctions between what is acceptable and what is not.

Pre-adolescents (10-13) face the challenge of developing "best friend" relationships and gaining acceptance from peers. A development task of pre-adolescents is figuring out how they are similar to and different from others. In attempting to understand themselves as unique individuals, they go through a stage during which close relations with same-sex "best friends" is very important. During this stage, they are very loyal to friends and greatly influenced by what friends think. Unfortunately, young adolescents can also be very exclusive in their peer groups such that those who are different are shunned or mocked. You probably see the importance of "best friends" in action on the deck quite often where being accepted and having someone to trust and confide in is of utmost importance. While this may, at times, hinder what you are attempting to do, keep in mind that it is a necessary part of social development and not an expression of disrespect on the part of the young athletes.

Adolescents (14-17 years) face the challenge of exploring who they are and how they fit into the world in which they live. During this stage, young people try to answer the question "who am I?" They go through processes of identity testing and identity formation - to a point that can be frustrating for the adults who know them! But adolescence is a time during which young people "try on" a variety of different identities in an attempt to discover and clarify values while exploring all the possibilities of who they might become as adults. What may seem like rebellion or acting out during this developmental stage, often may be athletes struggling to find identities that fit with their emerging sense of how they are connected to the world. We see this search for identity in the clothes they wear, the music they listen to, the activities they are involved in, the language they speak - and in the inconsistencies in their lifestyles.

As a coach, be tolerant and accepting of the various identities the athlete "tries on." Allow athletes to explore and test new and different identities as long as they do not put themselves in danger and as long as their actions are not in conflict with team goals or philosophy.

Older adolescents (16-19 years old) deal with the challenge of seeking Independence and Autonomy. A primary developmental task of adolescents is to move closer to being independent, autonomous beings — connected to but separate from others, in control of one's life but aware of limitations and boundaries. If we view autonomy on a spectrum with dependence on one end (as a newborn is totally dependent on caregivers) to independence on the other end of the spectrum (adult), we can view adolescents as attempting to move towards independence.

While complete independence and autonomy are not possible (nor is the individual ready for it), it is important that the athlete be allowed to make strides. If some autonomy is not allowed and encouraged, "swimming, or any organized sport, becomes a developmental dead end rather than a developmental opportunity" (J. Coakley). Feelings of independence and autonomy are derived, in part, from the sense that one has control over his or her life.

A Psychological Perspective

Another area of development that needs to be factored in relates to psychological, or cognitive, development. As with the other areas, this is an extensive area of study that we are not doing justice to when trying to condense the developmental process to a few concise points. That being said, let's try to identify and understand several elements of psychological development that may be especially important for coaches. These include the development of perceived competence, perspective-taking abilities, and motivation.

Perceived Competence: This concept of perceived competence is extremely important as it profoundly affects participation in sport, motivation, anxiety, and sport enjoyment. Athletes' perceptions of their athletic competence and sources they use to judge self-competence go through predictable developmental changes as is highlighted in the following:

— At an early age (seven-nine years), there is a focus on outcome and effort in judging one's competence. "I won, therefore I am a good swimmer" "I tried hard, I must be a good swimmer" Winning and losing serve as an important source of competence information for young athletes.

— From about ages eight-twelve, there is a gradual decline in the importance of feedback from parents as a source of competence information, an increase in coach technical knowledge as a source of competence information, and a gradual increase in the importance of peer comparison in making competence judgments. "I beat Joe which means I'm a good swimmer".

— The older athlete (twelve-thirteen) begins to recognize that both ability and effort impact performance. Prior to this, the athlete can not distinguish between the two concepts.

— There is a progression from focusing on peer comparison to focusing on self comparison (16-18 years) as sources of competence information.

— A "task or process" goal orientation increases with age with "outcome/win" goal orientation decreases with age.

We need to understand what sources children rely on to provide competence information. Because outcome is so important at a young age, our late maturing athletes are at risk of low competence as they are not experiencing much success. Additionally, note that coach feedback becomes an increasingly important source of competence information for athletes — recognize your role in enhancing (or tearing down) the athlete's sense of self-competence. For example, as opposed to just providing critical feedback ("you missed your last turn"), also reinforce what she did correctly ("you held your streamline and kick out").

Perspective-taking: the ability to take another's perspective progresses in a predictable sequence and impacts how an individual relates to others and overall behavior in the sport environment.

— At a young age (under eight), individuals are not able to take the perspective of others and, thus, have an egocentric perspective. The young athlete's thoughts, feelings, ideas, and needs are correct (as far as they are concerned)...and everyone else thinks and feels this same way too, right?

— Gradually, children develop the ability to take others' perspective but still view their perspective as the correct view.

— The latter stage of development occurs when the individual can take and appreciate another's perspective.

Motivation: simply defined as the direction and intensity of effort. Ideally, we want to see young athletes motivated to approach success in swimming with great intensity. But, what is it that motivates young athletes?

— Younger swimmers (seven-ten) seem more externally motivated while older swimmers are often more internally motivated.

— Around age seven-eight and older, young children begin seeing rewards as bribes ("discounting") which, under some conditions, can negatively affect motivation.

— While "discounting" increases with age, viewing extrinsic rewards (ribbons, medals, gold stars) as adding to intrinsic motivation decreases with age.

Although developmentally it may seem that extrinsic rewards undermine intrinsic motivation, this is not necessarily the case. Two aspects of the rewards are particularly important as they can affect intrinsic motivation — the controlling and informational aspects

— If rewards are being perceived as controlling ('swim fast to get a ribbon'), it decreases intrinsic motivation because they are doing it for reasons outside of themselves.

— The informational aspect of rewards affects intrinsic motivation by influencing one's self competence. Rewards that are given contingent on specific aspects of performance (and provide information about these specific aspects of performance) should enhance intrinsic motivation as they are providing positive feedback regarding the athlete's competence.

— The key is not the reward itself but the message behind the reward. The reward must be as providing positive competence information not as controlling behavior to enhance intrinsic motivation.

Athlete Development: Phases of Learning Model

Coaches, athletes and sport scientists alike have long sought to understand how to develop excellence or talent in individuals, and swimming is no exception. Fortunately, much work has been done in the field of talent development that we may be able to learn from in understanding the development of excellence in swimmers. Of most relevance is research by Benjamin Bloom in which he studied 120 individuals who had achieved excellence in a variety of domains (art, athletics, music, academics). He wanted to assess if common pathways to achieving excellence exist and, if so, to describe these pathways.

Bloom found that successful individuals went through similar phases of development and, furthermore, that the phases he identified were very similar to a 3 phase model of learning put forth years earlier by an educational researcher — thus adding greater support to his findings. It makes sense to think about applying this model of long-term development to young swimmers.

Early Maturation Versus Late Maturation

Children develop in sequential and predictable ways from young children into fully-grown 'adults. Yet, while individuals develop in similar ways, the timing of this maturation process can vary greatly. In fact, at any one chronological age individuals can vary by as much as five years maturationally. This means that with two swimmers who are chronologically eleven years old, one may by ten and the other fifteen biologically. The differences between ten and fifteen years of age is huge, as we all know, yet we are often training these athletes in the same way. A better approach is to consider the maturation process when working with young individuals. While we are generalizing about early maturers and late maturers and approaching them as two distinct groups, there is a lot of overlap in terms of all areas of development and their swim performance.

One way of trying to identify the kids who are going to be early maturers and late maturers is just by eyeballing them. In childhood, early maturers tend to be taller, heavier, and have more muscle mass than their peers. Alternately, late maturers are generally very light (smaller) and lean in childhood (ectomorphic). However, the late maturer may end up being taller as adults because they are in the childhood growth phase longer. This eyeball took at kids will give you, as the coach, a general idea of the young athletes likely to be early maturers and those likely to be late maturers. Other maturational characteristics include: arm-pit hair, facial hair, voice change, and/or menstrual cycle.

Another way for coaches to identify early maturers and late maturers is to track the athlete's growth. We know that, on average, children grow 2.5 inches a year and gain about five pounds a year until they hit their growth spurt. For girls, this growth spurt occurs roughly around age twelve-thirteen and around age fourteen-fifteen for boys. Tracking basic growth parameters twice a year will provide you with information regarding when the young athletes seem to be hitting their growth spurt. As an aside, taking these growth measures will also highlight those individuals who are not growing as would be expected — which may be an indication they are overtraining. Or, in the case of weight loss, the athletes may have some eating disturbances that need to be monitored and addressed.

In and of itself, being an early maturer or a late maturer is not a concern. However, the potential short-term and long-term ramifications if one ignores maturational differences are of concern. Early maturers, who hit their growth spurt prior to their same-aged (chronological) peers, tend to have an advantage in sports, especially sports requiring speed, power, and endurance where body mass is helpful. For biological reasons, not because of greater talent or ability, they are often able to outperform their peers. In childhood, they have much early success for which they receive reinforcement and recognition and, therefore, tend to initially stay with the sport.

Into high school we start seeing problems as the early maturer, who is used to experiencing success, gets frustrated because now all of a sudden peers are catching up with them. Others may ridicule and deride them because they are not experiencing the same outcome success and assume it is because they are not working hard, not putting forth the effort.

Part of the dropout we see around age 14 is due to early maturers leaving the sport out of frustration when they are not experiencing the same success as they did when they were younger. In reality; it's the physical changes that are occurring in their peers that are allowing others to catch up with them. We need to figure out a way to help our early maturers keep success in perspective. With late maturers, we have a different set of issues.

The late maturing kids often experience early failure because they are at a biological disadvantage (they are not as physically strong or developed) that affects performance outcomes. In the water, even though they may be working as hard, they often can't keep up with their peers which is a huge source of frustration. This leads to much ridicule by their peer group. These late maturers, who are not demonstrating success relative to their peers, then don't get the coaches' attention, encouragement, or recognition that their early maturing peers are getting. Unfortunately, in developmental sport programs, we often don't allow late maturers the time to let their physical maturity catch up and their skills to develop.

Instead, these children often leave the sport early because of lack of success and extreme frustration. This seems to hit late maturing boys the hardest because they are at an extreme disadvantage. Ironically, they could have the potential to be better athletes but we have to keep them involved at the younger ages to make sure they continue with their skill development. We need to figure out how to keep late maturers interested and involved in swimming despite a lack of early success.

Strategies to deal with early maturers and late maturers are;

— First, early success does not predict later success. This is nicety illustrated in a study looking at growth and development in boys (Medford Boys Growth Study) and its relation to sport abilities. Specifically, coaches were asked to rate kids in terms of their abilities in elementary school and again in junior high. They found that only

25% of the kids that were rated outstanding in elementary school were also rated as outstanding in terms of their abilities in junior high. This suggests that early talent/ ability is a poor predictor of future abilities since only one-fourth of the boys that demonstrated ability in elementary school also demonstrated ability in junior high.

— Given this, while it is tempting, we need to be cautious about focusing attention and energies into only the young athletes that are showing initial talent. The success demonstrated by early maturers is due to a biological advantage and, as we know, biological maturation is genetic. Remember that late maturers, who are at an initial physical disadvantage, don't have control over biology so let's not punish them for it.

— Education!! Make the athletes and their parents aware of some of the factors involved in why they are experiencing much success (as is the case with early maturers) or limited success (late maturers). An awareness of the situation will aid in keeping both success and failure in perspective white maintaining an eye towards individual skill development. Help them focus on long-term development rather than performance today.

— With early maturers, who have trouble keeping early success in perspective, we may want to think about moving them "up" in competitions so they are competing on a more level playing ground and get used to experiencing defeat. They can still practice with their peers (so social development is not affected) but compete against others of a similar maturational age.

— We need to search for strategies to keep late maturers involved in skill development programs as they are the ones getting left behind. We need to be creative in structuring situations so they can experience success and see improvement. Some examples may include: post and reward personal improvement in workout times which focuses the athlete on themselves rather than peer comparison; design team competitions that emphasize skill development; because peer comparison is natural, get the athletes to compare themselves to others of the same maturational age.

— For the most part, we train early and late maturers the same. This is unfortunate because the "window of opportunity" and peak performance occur earlier for early maturing athletes. Therefore, these athletes need to train more intensely earlier in their careers to maximize their potential.

— Gender plays a role on the influence of the maturation process on performance, dropout and self-esteem. Specifically, we need to pay special attention to early maturing females and late maturing males. An early maturing female develops a woman's body at a young age and becomes very self-conscious, especially in the swimsuits she must wear that reveals all. Conversely, the late maturing male is ridiculed for being small and also becomes very self-conscious which impacts his sense of self. White nothing can be done to remedy the situation, we need to help them in the area of self-confidence and self-worth.

Gender Difference in Training

In looking at development across the various disciplines, the notion of gender as a discriminating variable comes up again and again. That is, gender seems to be a factor involved in development across disciplines. However, caution is warranted: We don't want to separate males and females to such an extreme that we treat them as being on opposite ends of a spectrum. But, on the other hand, there are some gender-related differences that would be advantageous for coaches to at least be aware of. Ideally, we want to strike a balance between making young coaches sensitive enough to know gender-related differences but not so much so that they form incorrect stereotypes and over-generalize.

Given this, it seems beneficial to summarize (in no particular order) some of the more relevant gender-related differences and draw some implications or practical suggestions from this information:

Puberty

Boys reap the benefits of testosterone that is in full throttle at this time. There is an increase in muscle development due to increased testosterone — as testosterone is a protein anabolic that helps build up muscle by building up the protein that makes up the muscle. Concurrent with this increase in muscle mass is a decrease in percent body fat. All these changes are seemingly advantageous to the male swimmer. For females, puberty brings about an increase in the hormone estrogen. This increased estrogen is going to aid in laying down more fat and breaking down protein. Unlike males, development during puberty for females can initially have a deleterious effect on swim performance.

We have to make sure that the training programs that we're giving our girls at this time are going to help maintain their muscle and offset the natural physi-ological changes that are occurring. Additionally, we need to remember that increased fat deposits for woman is nature's way". It is not necessarily a change in her diet, changes in her training, or lack of willpower but is part of her development as a female that, to a large degree, is out of her control. As an aside, it has been suggested that because females tend to have less muscle mass than males during and after puberty, females may not need to taper as much in preparation for competition.

Sensitive Periods

From a physiological and growth perspective, boys and girls are different in terms of the timing of their 'sensitive periods' with girls maturing physiologically about two years ahead of boys. Remember, this sensitive period is a time when significant growth (aerobic development) can occur under the right conditions (training loads). While girls tend to mature earlier and thus have an earlier 'sensitive period', the real physiological variable is not gender but rather is the start of the growth curve. This growth spurt is really what should determine when to increase the aerobic phase. However, it is easier to understand and use this information when one knows that females tend to hit this growth phase at age 11-13 and males around age 13-15.

Because males tend to reach their growth spurt about two years after females, they are in childhood growth longer, which adds greater length to their legs. This leg length discrepancy tends to be what accounts for the height difference between males and females — how might longer legs impact performance in the water? We need to take advantage of these sensitive periods when training young athletes in order to maximize development. When entering this growth phase, which tends to happen earlier for females, coaches need to think about increasing aerobic training to maximize their capacities.

Stress Response

There have been some interesting findings on research looking at cortisol, which is a biochemical measure of physiological and psychological stress, in male and female swimmers. For an athlete with elevated cortisol values, it would be recommended that he/she closely monitor and possibly decrease training loads. In this research, it has been found that female swimmers (elite and sub-elite post-pubescent) have high cortisol values that stay high whereas males demonstrate natural ups and downs in cortisol values. This finding occurs under similar training yardage (similar physiological stress), which suggests the need to look at differences in psychological stress.

Interestingly, further analysis revealed that women coached by men had the highest cortisol all the time while the women swimmers coached by women had moderate levels like those seen in the male swimmers. This interesting finding not only suggests we may need to train males and females differently but that we also need to look at the interaction of athlete gender and coach gender. Because the differences seen in cortisol values occurs only within the female population, coaches (especially male coaches) may need to monitor the athlete's physiological and psychological adaptations to the imposed training stresses by observing behavior and communicating with the athlete.

There are numerous psychosocial developmental differences between young males and females. Let's present some of these differences - - you as the coach need to assess if you perceive these characteristics to exist in your athletes and how, if at all, it should impact your interaction with the athletes or the training environment you establish.

— Perceived competence in general, males tend to have higher perceptions of athletic competence than girls meaning they view themselves as more competent or able as athletes. And, we know that one's perception of competence influences such things as participation, enjoyment, and motivation.

— Extra steps may need to be taken to develop, bolster, and reinforce young girls' perceptions of competence; to help them recognize and appreciate their abilities as swimmers.

— Goal orientation findings are fairly consistent in showing that females are more task oriented and males are more oriented towards winning

— A win or outcome orientation suggests one focuses on comparing performance with and beating others whereas with a task goal orientation one is focused on comparing one's performance to personal standards and personal improvement. A task orientation has been tied to positive achievement related behaviors that we want to see in our young athletes.

— Given that only one athlete can "win" (which aren't very good odds), we may need to encourage boys to also compare performance relative to themselves as it greatly increases their chances of experiencing success and is much more within their control.

— Social/affiliation needs girls seems to have greater needs for affiliation and are more motivated to participate for social reasons whereas boys tend to be more motivated by competitive factors.

— If social factors are indeed important to your female athletes, it would be essential to make sure this need is being met; to incorporate time for social interaction in the training environment.

Dealing with Athletes Negetively Impacted by Growth Spurt

Maturation or natural growth and development tends to have a negative impact on females whereas it tends to be advantageous for males. With our female athletes, we often see an increase in percentage of body fat and a relative decrease, but not necessarily absolute decrease, in muscle mass. Following are a few practical strategies for dealing with this common challenge:

— Coaches need to be proactive by educating the athletes early on about why their performances may falter or plateau; prepare them for the growth and development and natural changes that will occur. If maturation brings about detriments in performance, help the athlete recognize why these performance decrements are occurring.

— In line with being proactive, make an effort, along the way, to teach kids coping skills to deal with adversity. They will then be better prepared to deal with this adversity.

— Be careful in not letting the highs get too high or the lows too low — keep it in perspective. It is crucial to not make a big deal out of success, and encourage parents not to as well.

— In some cases, having a female coach can help as she can relate better to the female athletes.

— Don't give up on the females as they are struggling with development; focus on having them give an honest effort in what they do.

— It seems that having a strong aerobic base and by having taken advantage of their window of opportunity for aerobic development is beneficial when trying to deal with their maturation and the ensuing changes.

— It may be beneficial to focus on training to think about decreasing the number of competitions until the athlete adjusts to her body and gets fit. It doesn't make sense to have the athlete 'beat her head against the wall', struggle with confidence, and experience failure and frustration.

— Coaches will typically have to help athletes make changes to their stroke technique to adjust to their bodies.

— Provide the young females with examples of athletes who have also experienced major body changes and have worked through them; find a role model or older athlete who had similar struggles and can talk to the younger athletes about how they coped.

Across sports, kids seem to be competing at younger and younger ages. Children as young as three, four, and five are competing in sports such as gymnastics, swimming, and baseball. As an extreme example, there is a competitive event called a "baby decathlon" in which infants compete against each other. Young children used to "play" with friends after school and on weekends, for a variety of reasons they now are enrolled in organized, competitive athletic programs. Should we be concerned? Can a child be too young for athletic competition?

When is a young swimmer ready to compete? While this is a seemingly simple question, it is actually quite complex with no easy answer. In addressing this question about readiness, first, we need to define what we mean by "competition". Then, we need to assess readiness across disciplines — from a biological, sociological, psychological, and physiological perspective — because, for example, a young athlete may be physiologically ready for the demands of competition but not psychologically ready. Only after readiness across disciplines has been examined can we try to answer this question with each of our young athletes.

What do we mean by competition? Restructuring competition to make it developmentally appropriate. When assessing readiness for competition, we tend to define competition strictly as organized swim meets where the participants compete against each other in specific events according to specific rules; a so called "adult model" of competition. A more fitting way of looking at competition involves broadening our definition of competi-tion to include models that are developmentally appropriate. A young athlete may not be socially, psychologically, technicality, or physiologically ready for the "adult model" of competition but would be ready for and benefit from more developmentally appropriate types of competition.

So, we need to think not so much about whether the young athlete is ready for competition and instead think about what type of competition the young athlete is ready for. In the following section, a few ideas or suggestions of competitions more appropriate for developmental athletes are presented. At the developmental level, the important element is skill; it therefore makes sense to structure events that emphasize skill. In addition, evaluating per-formance based strictly on time is an injustice to our late maturing athletes that are at a biological disadvantage rel-ative to their early maturing peers. Be creative in using different evaluation criteria or rewards that recognize areas we want to emphasize i.e., stroke, technique, individual improvement.

By creating developmental progressions for competition that are not part of our traditional rules and competitions, we are setting up a more sound and appropriate program for entry level swimmers to develop a firm foundation; a foundation that includes proper skill development and the development of self-esteem. Finally, creating a sound developmental program will instill in children a love of swimming.

As previously mentioned, because the question of readiness for competition is complex, the answer is also going to be complex. While we can not provide definitive answers regarding when precisely a child is ready for competition, we can 1) identify criteria or specific aspects of development that need to be met for the young athlete to be "ready" for swim competition (of the adult model); 2) discuss reasons why all young athletes are not developmentally ready for competition. Readiness issues regarding the areas of psychological and social development are discussed below. However, coaches must rely on their best judgement and knowledge of the swimmer to determine physical readiness for appropriate levels of competition.

As discussed in the psychological development section, the young athlete's perspective-taking ability develops sequentially and is important to understand because it impacts the young athlete's behavior in sport. In regards to this perspective-taking ability, in order to "compete" athletes need to be able to see the world from perspectives that go beyond their own personal perspective and see relationships that don't involve them directly. That is, they need to possess the cognitive abili-ties to take multiple perspectives or multiple roles. For the competition to be meaningful, the young athlete must be able to conceptualize the competition from an opponent's perspective and engage in social comparison.

It would not necessarily be harmful for the young athlete to compete without this perspective taking ability but the athlete's motivation and satisfaction would have to be derived elsewhere. Imposing a competitive reward structure on the sport activities of children who do not possess these social-cognitive skills is at best senseless and futile. Furthermore, as discussed earlier, research has identified sequential stages of development in terms of role taking abilities. And, it is not until around age twelve that individuals develop the ability to engage in formal reasoning and to put oneself in numerous roles. In sum, it seems that prior to age twelve (roughly) young children do not possess the social cognitive abilities to under-stand and experience the competitive process.

Another cognitive skill that impacts an athlete's readiness for competition involves how she explains performance outcomes, also termed "causal attributions". This cognitive skill is important not only because it illuminates aspects of performance that can be addressed in training but also because it impacts the athlete's perceptions of competence (a developmental skill discussed earli-er). For example, an athlete can attribute a loss to an unstable factor, such as lack of effort, and still feel competent in her abilities. Conversely, an athlete may attribute a loss to lack of ability, a stable factor, which will negatively impact his perceptions of self-competence. It has been found that prior to around age twelve, children are not able to distinguish between effort and ability in explaining successes and failures.

These young athletes, therefore, do not have the attributional abilities to accurately assess competence based on competitive performances. "These developmental shifts in causal reasoning influence not only how children of different ages will assess their competence based on performance outcomes but also how they will respond emotionally to those outcomes, what their future performance aspirations and success expectancies will be, and how they will approve or disapprove of other children based on those children's outcomes."

In trying to determine a young athlete's readiness for competition, we also need to assess if the athlete has the coping skills to deal with the demands and challenges inherent in the competitive environment. Some of these demands and challenges may include dealing with success and failure, managing time and energy at the competition, getting DQ'd, and performing in front of others. A young athlete who is found in tears after a race may not have the coping skills to deal with competition and is therefore not "ready" for competition. Coaches need to monitor how the young athlete copes with various situations in practice to determine if she has the coping skills to deal with the increased demands and challenges of competition. Use "teachable moments" in practice to help the athlete acquire coping skills.

There is a developmental need for social comparison beginning around five-six years of age. Yet, the above comments suggest that young athletes may not be ready for competition (adult model) until eleven-twelve years. We need to think about how we can fulfill this need for social comparison without adding additional stress/pressure that the athletes may not be ready for. We need to be creative in structuring opportunities for "healthy comparison". Now, back to our original question "can a child be too young for competition?" The answer would be "yes" if we are strictly referring to competition as competition of the adult model (i.e., organized swim meet) because, as has been dis-cussed, young athletes often do not have the psychological, social, and physical skills necessary for the competitive envi-ronment. However, if we structure competition to make it developmentally appropriate for these young athletes, they can benefit from the experience and develop the skills to prepare themselves for competition.

Health, Fitness, and Physical Activity

Over the past 50 years there has been considerable change in the definitions of terms such as physical fitness and even health. New terms have evolved such as wellness and metabolic fitness. For ease of understanding, we have grouped the definitions in two broad categories: Product and Process. Products refer to states of being such as physical fitness, health and wellness. These are also commonly referred to as outcomes and they are frequently used as dependent measures in research. Process refers to behaviors or lifestyles and these are frequently used as independent measures for research purposes. Examples of processes or lifestyle behaviors are physical activity, exercise, sports, dance, etc.

Physical Fitness

A set of attributes that people have or achieve relating to their ability to perform physical activity. An alternative definition that provides additional descriptive information is also included here. Physical fitness is a state of well-being with low risk of premature health problems and energy to participate in a variety of physical activitie. While either is a good definition, most experts agree that physical fitness is both multidimensional and hierarchical.

Bouchard, Shephard, and Stephens presented a comprehensive model for physical fitness that includes morphological fitness, bone strength, muscular fitness, flexibility, motor fitness, cardiovascular fitness, and metabolic fitness.

Physical Fitness		Skills	
Physiological	Health-Related	Skill-Related	Sports
	Metabolic	Body	Agility Team Composition
Morphological	Cardiovascular	Balance Fitness	Individual
Bone Integrity	Flexibility	Coordination	Lifetime
Other	Muscular Endurance	Power	Other
	Muscle Strength	Speed	
		Reaction Time	
		Other	

Figure 1. Common Physical Fitness and Fitness Related Terms

Health-Related Physical Fitness

Health-related physical fitness consists of those components of physical fitness that have a relationship with good health. The components are commonly defined as body composition, cardiovascular fitness, flexibility, muscular endurance, and strength.

Prior to the last 40 years the distinction between health-related physical fitness and skill-related physical fitness was not typically made. When tests of physical fitness are administered in school, medical and other settings it is typically health-related fitness components that are measured. Typically lab and field tests of health-related fitness involve some type of performance such as running, stretching, or doing a specific muscle exercise. Because body composition is not a performance measure, some question its inclusion as a component of health-related physical fitness. Possessing good health-related fitness is related to lower risk of illness and improved quality of life.

Body Composition

A health-related component of physical fitness that relates to the relative amounts of muscle, fat, bone and other vital parts of the body.

This component of physical fitness is measured in the laboratory using such measures as underwater weighing and in the field using skinfold calipers. There are a variety of other methods of assessing body composition; also referred to as relative leanness. As noted previously body composition is the only non-performance measure among the health-related physical fitness components.

Cardiovascular Fitness

A health-related component of physical fitness that relates to ability of the circulatory and respiratory systems to supply oxygen during sustained physical activity.

Cardiovascular fitness is also referred to as cardiovascular endurance, aerobic fitness and cardiorespiratory fitness. A Max V•O2 test in the laboratory setting is considered to be the best measure of cardiovascular fitness. Commonly administered field tests include the mile run, the 12 minute run, the 1 mile run, the mile walk, the PACER run for children and various bicycle, step, and treadmill tests.

Flexibility

A health-related component of physical fitness that relates to the range of motion available at a joint.

Some experts specifiy that flexibility requires range of motion without discomfort or pain. Flexibility is specific to each joint of the body, thus there is no general measurement of flexibility as there is for cardiovascular fitness. Flexibility is typically measured in the lab using measurement devices such as a goniometer, flexometer and in the field with tests such as the sit and reach and the zipper.

Muscular Endurance

A health-related component of physical fitness that relates to the muscle's ability to continue to perform without fatigue.

Like flexibility, muscular endurance is specific in nature. For true assessment of muscular endurance it would be necessary to test each major muscle group of the body. Lab and field tests of muscular endurance are similar and are based on the number of repetitions that can be performed by the specific muscle group being tested (example: repetitions of push-ups or abdominal curls. Muscular endurance can be measured isometrically (static contractions) or isotonically (dynamic contractions).

Strength

A health-related component of physical fitness that relates to the ability of the muscle to exert force.

Like flexibility and muscular endurance, strength is specific in nature. For true assessment it would be necessary to test each major muscle group of the body. Lab and field tests are similar and involve the assessment of one repetition maximum. 1RM tests are typically conducted on resistance machines. Strength can also be assessed using dynamometers. Strength can be measured isometrically (static contractions) or isotonically (dynamic contractions).

Skill-related Physical Fitness

Skill-related physical fitness consists of those components of physical fitness that have a relationship with enhanced performance in sports and motor skills. The components are commonly defined as agility, balance, coordination, power, speed and reaction time.

With the changing focus to health-related physical fitness those components of fitness previously included in fitness tests that are not directly related to improved health were designated as skill-related physical fitness components. Possession of skill-related fitness abilities enhances ability to perform in sports and games but only has an indirect connection with health. The skill-related components of fitness are considered to be agility, balance, coordination, power, speed, and reaction time though some experts feel that other abilities such as visual tracking should be included.

It is assumed that people who possess skill-related fitness will be more likely to engage in regular activity and for this reason will have enhanced health-related fitness and a lower risk of hypokinetic diseases and condition. Skill-related fitness components are assessed with performance measures. Such components as reaction time and speed are considered by some to be more related to heredity than healthy lifestyles, especially in children.

Agility

A skill-related component of physical fitness that relates to the ability to rapidly change the position of the entire body in space with speed and accuracy. Agility is typically measured using a shuttle or zig-zag run. Tests of agility are common as screening tests among sports teams.

Balance

A skill-related component of physical fitness that relates to the maintenance of equilibrium while stationary or moving. Balance is typically measured using a balance beam or tests that require holding a stationary posture after changing body positions. Balance is generally considered to be of two types; static and dynamic.

Coordination

A skill-related component of physical fitness that relates to the ability to use the senses, such as sight and hearing, together with body parts in performing motor tasks smoothly and accurately. Coordination is typically assessed using measures of hand-eye or foot-eye coordination such as juggling, dribbling a ball or hitting an object. There are, however, many different types of coordination and total assessment of coordination would require many different tests.

Power

A skill-related component of physical fitness that relates to the ability to the rate at which one can perform work. Power is considered to be a combination of strength and speed. It has also been defined as the ability to exert muscle force quickly (Howley and Franks). For this reason some consider it to be a combination of skill and health-related physical fitness. Examples of power include putting the shot and vertical jumping. There are, however, many different types of power and total assessment would require many different tests.

Speed

A skill-related component of physical fitness that relates to the ability to perform a movement within a short period of time. There are many different types of speed such as running speed, swimming speed, speed of hand or foot movement to name but a few. Among athletes a 40 yard dash is often used to measure speed. There are a wide variety of laboratory measures of speed that are highly specific to different body parts and different human movement activities.

Reaction Time

A skill-related component of physical fitness that relates to the time elapsed between stimulation and the beginning of the reaction to it. An example of reaction time is moving your foot from the accelerator to the brake pedal when reacting to a situation that requires a person to stop a car. This example illustrates the fact that in many cases, the total response time is the more important variable. Total response time includes stimulus to beginning of movement (reaction time) to end of movement (movement time). Like other measures of skill-related fitness there are many different types of reaction time and total assessment of reaction time would require many different tests. Sophisticated timing devices are used to measure total response time in the lab. Like speed, reaction time is considered to be a component of fitness that is greatly influenced by heredity.

Physiological Fitness

Physiological fitness includes non-performance components of physical fitness that relate to biological systems that are influenced by one's level of habitual physical activity. The concept of physiological fitness was introduced in a publication of the first international consensus statement of current knowledge of physical activity. It differentiated health-related (primarily performance measures) from non-performance measures. Some of these measures are defined below. Some of the sub-components of physiological fitness that have gained acceptance are metabolic fitness, morphological fitness, and bone integrity.

Metabolic Fitness

The state of metabolic systems and variables predictive of the risk for diabetes and cardiovascular disease which can be favorably altered by increased physical activity or regular endurance exercise without the requirement of a training-related increase inV•O2max.

Though Depres, et al. are first credited with using the term metabolic fitness it was first used widely after it was described in the proceedings of the second International Consensus Conference on Physical Activity, Fitness and Health. The use of the term metabolic fitness in the recent position statement describing the quality and quantity of physical activity needed to attain health-related benefits establishes it as a major fitness component. The International Consensus statement noted that metabolic fitness included such sub-components as blood sugar levels, blood lipid levels, and blood hormone levels. The reason for the identification of metabolic fitness as a separate component of fitness is because "...it is now clear that lower levels of physical activity (particularly intensity) than recommended (by this position stand) may reduce the risk for certain chronic degenerative diseases and improve metabolic fitness and yet may not be of sufficient quantity or quality to improve VO2max."

Morphological Fitness

A non-performance component of fitness related to body composition factors such as body circumferences, body fat content, and regional body fat distribution.

Morphological fitness measures are often related to metabolic fitness components. As noted earlier body composition is often included as a component of health-related fitness but is also appropriately considered a component of morphological fitness. Those measures used to assess body composition are also used to assess morphological fitness as are measures such as body mass index, waist circumference, and waist to hip ratio.

Bone Integrity (Bone Strength)

A non-performance component of fitness related to bone mineral density. Bone strength was identified as a component of physical fitness in the first International Consensus Statement. Because measurement is expensive and requires special instrumentation and a high degree of expertise, there are no currently used field measures that are used extensively. There is general consensus, however, that bone integrity is related to habitual physical activity.

Motor Skills

Motor skills are non-fitness abilities that improve with practice (learning) and relate to one's ability to perform specific sports and other motor tasks.

Though motor skills are not considered to be part of physical fitness, they are related to successful performance in physical activity. Motor skills are sometimes confused with skill-related fitness abilities. In fact, they are quite different. Skill-related fitness components enhance one's ability to learn sports and motor skills quickly and are related to one's ability to achieve high level performance. Examples of motor skills are a tennis serve, shooting a basketball, and kicking a football. A line (Figure 1) is used to indicate the fact that motor skills are not components of physical fitness. There are many different kinds of motor skills—only those associated with sports are included in Figure 1.

Hypokinetic Diseases or Conditions

Hypokinetic diseases are conditions related to inactivity or low levels of habitual activity. The term "hypokinetic" was coined by Kraus and Raab in their book Hypokinetic Disease. This term is now widely accepted and can be used to describe many of the diseases and conditions associated with inactivity and poor fitness such as those conditions outlined in Physical Activity and Health: A Report of the Surgeon General.

Health

Health is a state of being associated with freedom from disease and illness that also includes a positive component (wellness) that is associated with a quality of life and positive well-being. More than 50 years ago the World Health Organization defined health as more than freedom from illness, disease, and debilitating conditions. Recent public health documents have acknowledged the positive component of health (wellness).

Wellness

Wellness is a state of being describing a state of positive health in the individual and comprising biological and psychological well-being as exemplified by quality of life and a sense of well-being.

The suggestion by the World Health Organization that health had a positive component led to the use of the term wellness. The term wellness is now widely used to describe the state of being representing the positive component of health. The Health Goals for the Nation for the Year 2010 uses quality of life measures such as self-rated health, a healthy days index, and an activity days indicators of health and wellness. Other wellness or quality of life indicators include vitality, hardiness, and vigor.

Quality of Life

A term that connotes an overall sense of well being. Kaplan and Bush introduced the term health-related quality of life (HRQL). However, for public health use, two types of global quality of life are identified: health-related quality of life and quality of life (not health related). Health related quality of life is limited to those aspects that can clearly be shown to affect mental or physical health. Examples include functional status and well-being. Non-health related quality of life includes such factors as happiness and life satisfaction. Individual quality of life is identified as related to specific people or individuals. Community quality of life relates to groups of people or communities.

Healthy Lifestyles or Behaviors

There are many healthy lifestyles or behaviors that contribute to fitness, health and wellness. In this section the processes or healthy lifestyles that are defined relate only to one healthy lifestyle: physical activity.

Physical Activity

Bodily movement that is produced by the contraction of skeletal muscle and that substantially increases energy expenditure. The first International Consensus statement on physical activity, fitness and health suggested that physical activity was an umbrella term (Figure 2) that was that had multiple dimensions. Forms of physical activity such as exercise, sports, dance (among others) are considered as sub-categories of physical activity. Only selected forms of physical activity, including those defined in the first international consensus statement are defined here.

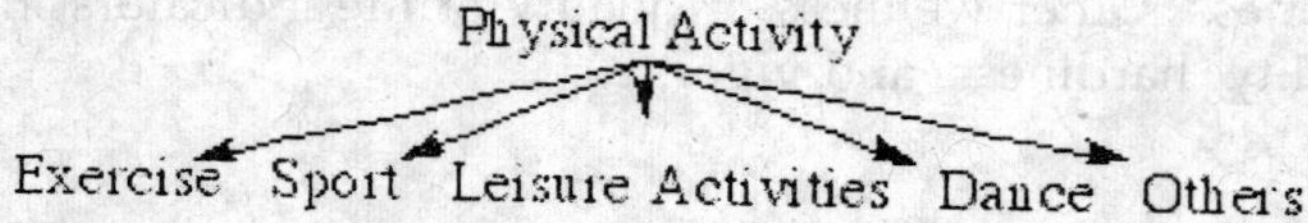

Figure 2. The sub-categories of physical activity

Exercise (training)

Exercise is leisure time physical activity conducted with the intention of developing physical fitness. Since the first International Consensus statement on physical activity, fitness and health the distinction has been made between physical activity and exercise noting that exercise is a specific form of physical activity dedicated to improving physical fitness. Physical training is another term that is used as a synonym for exercise.

Leisure Activity

Leisure activity is physical activity undertaken during discretionary time. Research in physical activity often separates leisure physical activity from vocational activity. Leisure activity includes exercise but all forms of leisure activities are not exercise.

Fundamentals of Physical Fitness

You have taken the important first step on the path to physical fitness by seeking information. The next step is to decide that you are going to be physically fit. This pamphlet is designed to help you reach that decision and your goal. The decision to carry out a physical fitness program cannot be taken lightly. It requires a lifelong commitment of time and effort. Exercise must become one of those things that you do without question, like bathing and brushing your teeth. Unless you are convinced of the benefits of fitness and the risks of unfitness, you will not succeed.

Patience is essential. Don't try to do too much too soon and don't quit before you have a chance to experience the rewards of improved fitness. You can't regain in a few days or weeks what you have lost in years of sedentary living, but you can get it back if your persevere. And the prize is worth the price. In the following pages you will find the basic information you need to begin and maintain a personal physical fitness program. These guidelines are intended for the average healthy adult. It tells you what your goals should be and how often, how long and how hard you must exercise to achieve them. It also includes information that will make your workouts easier, safer and more satisfying. The rest is up to you.

Checking Your Health

If you're under 35 and in good health, you don't need to see a doctor before beginning an exercise program. But if you are over 35 and have been inactive for several years, you should consult your physician, who may or may not recommend a graded exercise test. Other conditions that indicate a need for medical clearance are:

— High blood pressure.

— Heart trouble.

— Family history of early stroke or heart attack deaths.

— Frequent dizzy spells.

— Extreme breathlessness after mild exertion.

— Arthritis or other bone problems.

— Severe muscular, ligament or tendon problems.

— Other known or suspected disease.

Vigorous exercise involves minimal health risks for persons in good health or those following a doctor's advice. Far greater risks are presented by habitual inactivity and obesity.

Physical fitness is to the human body what fine tuning is to an engine. It enables us to perform up to our potential. Fitness can be described as a condition that helps us look, feel and do our best. More specifically, it is:

> "The ability to perform daily tasks vigorously and alertly, with energy left over for enjoying leisure- time

activities and meeting emergency demands. It is the ability to endure, to bear up, to withstand stress, to carry on in circumstances where an unfit person could not continue, and is a major basis for good health and well-being."

Physical fitness involves the performance of the heart and lungs, and the muscles of the body. As you undertake your fitness program, it's important to remember that fitness is an individual quality that varies from person to person. It is influenced by age, sex, heredity, personal habits, exercise and eating practices. You can't do anything about the first three factors. However, it is within your power to change and improve the others where needed.

Physical fitness is most easily understood by examining its components, or "parts." There is widespread agreement that these four components are basic:

— *Cardiorespiratory Endurance*: the ability to deliver oxygen and nutrients to tissues, and to remove wastes, over sustained periods of time. Long runs and swims are among the methods employed in measuring this component.

— *Muscular Strength*: the ability of a muscle to exert force for a brief period of time. Upper-body strength, for example, can be measured by various weight-lifting exercises.

— *Muscular Endurance*: the ability of a muscle, or a group of muscles, to sustain repeated contractions or to continue applying force against a fixed object. Pushups are often used to test endurance of arm and shoulder muscles.

— *Flexibility*: the ability to move joints and use muscles through their full range of motion. The sit-and- reach test is a good measure of flexibility of the lower back and backs of the upper legs.

Body Composition is often considered a component of fitness. It refers to the makeup of the body in terms of lean mass (muscle, bone, vital tissue and organs) and fat mass. An optimal ratio of fat to lean mass is an indication of fitness, and the right types of exercises will help you decrease body fat and increase or maintain muscle mass. How often, how long and how hard you exercise, and what kinds of exercises you do should be determined by what you are trying to accomplish. Your goals, your present fitness level, age, health, skills, interest and convenience are among the factors you should consider. For example, an athlete training for high-level competition would follow a different program than a person whose goals are good health and the ability to meet work and recreational needs.

Your exercise program should include something from each of the four basic fitness components described previously. Each workout should begin with a warmup and end with a cooldown. As a general rule, space your workouts throughout the week and avoid consecutive days of hard exercise. Here are the amounts of activity necessary for the average healthy person to maintain a minimum level of overall fitness. Included are some of the popular exercises for each category.

— *Warmup*: 5-10 minutes of exercise such as walking, slow jogging, knee lifts, arm circles or trunk rotations. Low intensity movements that simulate movements to be used in the activity can also be included in the warmup.

— *Muscular strendth*: a minimum of two 20-minute sessions per week that include exercises for all the major muscle groups. Lifting weights is the most effective way to increase strength.

— *Muscular endurance*: at least three 30-minute sessions each week that include exercises such as calisthenics, pushups, situps, pullups, and weight training for all the major muscle groups.

— *Cardiorespiratory endurance*: at least three 20-minute bouts of continuous aerobic (activity requiring oxygen) rhythmic exercise each week. Popular aerobic conditioning activities include brisk walking, jogging, swimming, cycling, rope-jumping, rowing, cross-country skiing, and some continuous action games like racquetball and handball.

— *Flexibility*: 10-12 minutes of daily stretching exercises performed slowly, without a bouncing motion. This can be included after a warmup or during a cooldown.

— *Cool down*: a minimum of 5-10 minutes of slow walking, low-level exercise, combined with stretching.

The keys to selecting the right kinds of exercises for developing and maintaining each of the basic components of fitness are found in these principles:

— *Specificity*: pick the right kind of activities to affect each component. Strength training results in specific strength changes. Also, train for the specific activity you're interested in. For example, optimal swimming performance is best achieved when the muscles involved in swimming are trained for the movements required. It does not necessarily follow that a good runner is a good swimmer.

— *Overload*: work hard enough, at levels that are vigorous and long enough to overload your body above its resting level, to bring about improvement.

— *Regularity*: you can't hoard physical fitness. At least three balanced workouts a week are necessary to maintain a desirable level of fitness.

— *Progression*: increase the intensity, frequency and/or duration of activity over periods of time in order to improve.

Some activities can be used to fulfill more than one of your basic exercise requirements. For example, in addition to increasing cardiorespiratory endurance, running builds muscular endurance in the legs, and swimming develops the arm, shoulder and chest muscles. If you select the proper activities, it is possible to fit parts of your muscular endurance workout into your cardiorespiratory workout and save time.

Measuring Your Heart Rate

Heart rate is widely accepted as a good method for measuring intensity during running, swimming, cycling, and other aerobic activities. Exercise that doesn't raise your heart rate to a certain level and keep it there for 20 minutes won't contribute significantly to cardiovascular fitness. The heart rate you should maintain is called your target heart rate. There are several ways of arriving at this figure. One of the simplest is: maximum heart rate (220 - age) x 70%. Thus, the target heart rate for a 40 year-old would be 126. Some methods for figuring the target rate take individual differences into consideration. Here is one of them:

— Subtract age from 220 to find maximum heart rate.

— Subtract resting heart rate (see below) from maximum heart rate to determine heart rate reserve.

— Take 70% of heart rate reserve to determine heart rate raise.

— Add heart rate raise to resting heart rate to find target rate.

Resting heart rate should be determined by taking your pulse after sitting quietly for five minutes. When checking heart rate during a workout, take your pulse within five seconds after interrupting exercise because it starts to go down once you stop moving. Count pulse for 10 seconds and multiply by six to get the per-minute rate.

Control Your Wieght

The key to weight control is keeping energy intake (food) and energy output (physical activity) in balance. When you consume only as many calories as your body needs, your weight will usually remain constant. If you take in more calories than your body needs, you will put on excess fat. If you expend more energy than you take in you will burn excess fat. Exercise plays an important role in weight control by increasing energy output, calling on stored calories for extra fuel. Recent studies show that not only does exercise increase metabolism during a workout, but it causes your metabolism to stay increased for a period of time after exercising, allowing you to burn more calories.

How much exercise is needed to make a difference in your weight depends on the amount and type of activity, and on how much you eat. Aerobic exercise burns body fat. A medium-sized adult would have to walk more than 30 miles to burn up 3,500 calories, the equivalent of one pound of fat. Although that may seem like a lot, you don't have to walk the 30 miles all at once. Walking a mile a day for 30 days will achieve the same result, providing you don't increase your food intake to negate the effects of walking.

If you consume 100 calories a day more than your body needs, you will gain approximately 10 pounds in a year. You could take that weight off, or keep it off, by doing 30 minutes of moderate exercise daily. The combination of exercise and diet offers the most flexible and effective approach to weight control. Since muscle tissue weighs more than fat tissue, and exercise develops muscle to a certain degree, your bathroom scale won't necessarily tell you whether or not you are "fat." Well-muscled individuals, with relatively little body fat, invariably are "overweight" according to standard weight charts.

If you are doing a regular program of strength training, your muscles will increase in weight, and possibly your overall weight will increase. Body composition is a better indicator of your condition than body weight. Lack of physical activity causes muscles to get soft, and if food intake is not decreased, added body weight is almost always fat. Once-active people, who continue to eat as they always have after settling into sedentary lifestyles, tend to suffer from "creeping obesity."

Clothing

All exercise clothing should be loose-fitting to permit freedom of movement, and should make the wearer feel comfortable and self-assured. As a general rule, you should wear lighter clothes than temperatures might indicate. Exercise generates great amounts of body heat. Light-colored clothing that reflects the sun's rays is cooler in the summer, and dark clothes are warmer in winter. When the weather is very cold, it's better to wear several layers of light clothing than one or two heavy layers. The extra layers help trap heat, and it's easy to shed one of them if you become too warm.

In cold weather, and in hot, sunny weather, it's a good idea to wear something on your head. Wool watch or ski caps are recommended for winter wear, and some form of tennis or sailor's hat that provides shade and can be soaked in water is good for summer. Never wear rubberized or plastic clothing, such garments interfere with the evaporation of perspiration and can cause body temperature to rise to dangerous levels. The most important item of equipment for the runner is a pair of sturdy, properly-fitting running shoes. Training shoes with heavy, cushioned soles and arch supports are preferable to flimsy sneakers and light racing flats.

Time to Exercise

The hour just before the evening meal is a popular time for exercise. The late afternoon workout provides a welcome change of pace at the end of the work day and helps dissolve the day's worries and tensions. Another popular time to work out is early morning, before the work day begi1ns. Advocates of the early start say it makes them more alert and energetic on the job. Among the factors you should consider in developing your workout schedule are personal preference, job and family responsibilities, availability of exercise facilities and weather.

It's important to schedule your workouts for a time when there is little chance that you will have to cancel or interrupt them because of other demands on your time. You should not exercise strenuously during extremely hot, humid weather or within two hours after eating. Heat and/or digestion both make heavy demands on the circulatory system, and in combination with exercise can be an overtaxing double load.

Physical Fitness is generally defined as a set of abilities that an individual possesses in order to perform specific types of physical activity efficiently and effectively. Fitness consists of at least eleven different components which are largely independent of each other but which overlap in complex ways. These components of Physical Fitness may be categorized into - Performance related fitness components and Health related fitness components. Each component of fitness is influenced by a different part of the body or body systems. Because the different components of fitness are independent of one another it is possible to be well developed in one or more while being below par in others.

Health Related Fitness (HRL)

Health Related Fitness (HRL) is the ability of the body to meet the demands of daily physical effort and activity, to have enough energy reserve for unexpected emergencies and to enjoy the feeling of well being that regular exercise brings.

— *Muscular enduerance*: The ability of the muscles to repeatedly exert themselves over a period of time.

— *Strength*: The ability of the musces to exert maximum force

— *Cardio-vascular endurance*: is the ability of the heart,blood vessels, blood and respiratory system to supply oxygen and fuel to the muscles at a steady rate for a considerable length of time

— *Flexibility*: The ability to move the body joints through the full range of motion (ROM) without discomfort or pain.

— *Body composition*: The relative percentage of muscle fat bone and other tissues that comprise the body.

— *Performance Related fitness (PRF) components*: Performance Related fitness (PRF) components are associated more with performance than good health. To compete in selected sporting activities one develops a high level of Health related fitness plus Performance related fitness.. eg. moderate amounts of strength are required to prevent back problems in daily life, whereas high levels of strength (HRF) and power (PRF) contribute most to improved performance in strength based competitve avtivites such as weight lifting.

PRF components include - Agility, Reaction Time, Power, Co - ordination, Balance and Speed. It should be noted that some PRF components may be deemed as HRF components in certain groups of society eg. elderly

— *Agility*: The ability to quickly and accurately change the direction of the movement of the entire body in space.

— *Balance*: The ability to maintain equilibrium while stationary or moving.

— *Coordination*: The ability to combine the senses with the body parts to perform activities smoothly and accurately. (eg.Hand - eye and Foot - eye)

— *Reaction Time*: The time elapsed between stimulation and the start of reaction to that stimulation.

— *Power*: The ability to transfer energy into force at a fast rate.

— *Speed*: The ability to perform a movement in a short period of time

Principles of Training

Certain principles must be followed if an athlete is to make steady progress in practices and training programmes and to avoid illness and injury. These Principles can be applied when developing any or all of the Components of Fitness. These principles are Specificity, Overload, Progression, Recuperation, Reversibility

1. *Specificity*: Training will only improve those parts of the body being trained e.g. stretching the hamstring will increase the hamstrings flexibility, long distance running will increase cardio vascular endurance. Therefore, training should reflect the type of fitness required for whatever sport is being trained. To develop C.V. endurance the aerobic system (Heart/Lungs) must be trained to show improvement. Any activity where the body is requires to work at a continuous steady pace for a long period of time will improve Cardio - Vascular Endurance eg. Swimming, walking, cycling jogging etc.

2. *Overload (Milo Story)*: To become more efficient the specific body systems must be exercised at a level above that which can be carried out comfortably i.e. training must exceed the typical daily demand and the body should be worked harder than usual. This increased demand can be achieved by increasing -

— Frequency

— Intensity

— Time

(These three factors are commonly addressed using the acronym FIT, often an extra T is added giving FITT to account for Type of activity to incorporate the principle of specificity.)

3. *Progression*: Progression is a continuation of the Overload principle but refers to gradually increasing the overload over time and not all at once. If one progresses too rapidly they may be in danger of becoming demotivated, fail to reach their goals or injured.

4. *Recuperation*: Training cannot be rushed. The body requires time for the improvement in physiological mechanisms to be implemented. Typical improvements include:

— Improved respiration, heart function, circulation and blood volume.

— Improved muscular endurance, strength and power.

— Tougher bones, ligaments, tendons and connective tissue.

Overload training must not be done daily as it can damage muscle fibers and time must be allowed for muscles to heal. If training intensity is increased too quickly this can lead to increased risk of illness, injury, fatigue or cause one to peak too quickly.

5. *Reversibility*: As the cliché says "Use it or loose it". Unfortunately, it usually takes longer to develop endurance than to lose it, as muscles quickly lose their ability to use oxygen efficiently. In fact with complete bed rest fitness can decline at a rate of almost 10% per week! Therefore, a balance must be found between exercise and rest.

Fitt

The acronym FITT is the formula used to establish "prescriptions" for individual needs and goals when developing Cardio - Vascular Endurance. It is an extension of the Overload Principle. It is similar to the type of information that doctors use when prescribing medicines. eg. Take 1 pill(Intensity) called "cure"(Type), twice a day(Frequency), for two weeks(Time).

Frequency: How often do you exercise?

In order to improve C.V. endurance one needs to implement a regular programme of aerobic training on a regular basis. Initially 3 - 4 times a week is recommended thereby balancing the Principles of Recuperation and Progression.

Intensity: The difficulty of the exercise.

There is a range within which the heart needs to work to best develop C.V. endurance. This is called the Target Training Zone.

Time: The duration of the exercise.

Initially, this should be at least 20 mins. Then increase the duration as one increases their endurance levels.

Type: *The activity must be specific to the desired fitness component*

The type of training activity must be specific to or closely related to the intended activity. One should try to vary the activity to keep it interesting and motivating. Aerobic type activities include any activity where the individual works at a steady, continuous pace for a long period of time eg.walking, cycling. jogging, aerobics etc. Popular methods of training include - interval, continuous and Fartlek training.

Warm - Up and Cool - Down

Warm - Up:Pupose and Structure

To gradually prepare the body for more demanding activity. The warm - up should consist of three parts -

— Pulse - raiser -gradually increase body temperature and heart rate thereby increase blood flow to the muscles

— Joint mobilisation - to reduce the risk of injury and prepare the body for activity

— Stretch -to reduce the risk of injury and to prepare the body for activity.

Cool - Down: Pupose and Structure

To allow the body to recover gradually and return to its resting level. The Cool - down should consist of ;

— Pulse - lowerer

— Post stretch begins to remove the lactate build up.

— Stretching allows the muscle fibres to return to their starting form and help start repair any damaged fibres.

Where possible both the warm - up and cool - down should be linked to the activity being practiced.

Cardio - Vascular Endurance

Cardio - Vascular Endurance is the ability of the heart,blood vessels, blood and respiratory system to supply oxygen and fuel to the muscles at a steady rate for a considerable length of time

Biological Basis for Aerobic Endurance

1. The ability of the respiratory system to take air into the body and the efficiency with which the lungs supply oxygen to the blood. Endurance is reduced if your breathing is inefficient or if the lungs are not working well.
2. The ability of the blood to carry oxygen. This can be reduced if you are ill, have a poor diet or train too hard
3. The ability of your heart to pump blood around your body
4. The efficiency of the circulatory system that takes blood to your muscles and then returns it to your heart.
5. The ability of your muscles to extract oxygen from your blood.
6. Heredity influences your level of Cardio Vscular Endurance

Changes to the C.V. system during Aerobic activity

— The heart pumps faster and pumps more blood.

— Lungs increase volume of air inhaled and exhaled.

— Muscles contract at a greater speed.

— Body temperature rises and the body sweats.

Benefits of C.V. development are:

— The heart becomes more efficient
— Blood volume. red cells and haemoglobin increases
— Decreases resting resting blood pressure
— Arteries grow larger
— Diaphragm grows stronger
— Lungs become more expandable increasing in volume
— Decreases body fat
— Increases energy level
— Recovery after exercise becomes quicker
— Reduces risk of heart disease, other hypokenetic conditions.
— Reduces the risk of kopan early death.

Popular methods of improving Cardio - Vascular Endurance:

— *Interval training*: This is a combination of low intensity activity and high intensity actiivity.

— *Continuous training*: This is training without a rest and is performed at moderate intensity (70% of MHR approx) To be effective the activity needs to last at least 15 minutes (Time) and needs to be done at least three times a week (Frequency)

— *Fartlek "Speed Play" training*: Originates in Sweden, and translates to mean "Speed Play." The speed at which the athlete is moving varies greatly threoughout the training session - anything from walking to sprinting. It combines both aerobic and anaerobic development, therefore it needs to be carefully planned.

— *Circuit training*: Circuit training involves using different areas of a gym, sportshall or any obstacle free indoor or outdoor space. It consists of a number of different exercise areas specific to the individuals training goals.(developing in this case Cardio vascular enduarance). Each exercise area is called a station.

After completing the exercise at one station the individual moves on to the next station. The activities differ so that different muscle groups are used at each station, allowing time for muscle recovery and increasing motivation through variety. A set time is spent at each station with a set recovery time between stations allowing for recovery and individuals to move on to the next station. Circuits can cater for a large number of people. Circuits require a minimum amount of equipment and space. Circuits are highly adaptable for different sports.It can be skill or fitness orientated or both.

Physical Activity: Fundamental to Preventing Disease

Regular physical activity, fitness, and exercise are critically important for the health and well being of people of all ages. Research has demonstrated that virtually all individuals can benefit from regular physical activity, whether they participate in vigorous exercise or some type of moderate health-enhancing physical activity. Even among frail and very old adults, mobility and functioning can be improved through physical activity. Therefore, physical fitness should be a priority for Americans of all ages.

Regular physical activity has been shown to reduce the morbidity and mortality from many chronic diseases. Millions of Americans suffer from chronic illnesses that can be prevented or improved through regular physical activity:

— 12.6 million people have coronary heart disease;

— 1.1 million people suffer from a heart attack in a given year;

— 17 million people have diabetes; about 90% to 95% of cases are type 2 diabetes, which is associated with obesity and physical inactivity; approximately 16 million people have 'pre diabetes';

— 107,000 people are newly diagnosed with colon cancer each year;

— 300,000 people suffer from hip fractures each year;

— 50 million people have high blood pressure; and

— Nearly 50 million adults (between the ages of 20 and 74), or 27% of the adult population, are obese; overall more than 108 million adults, or 61% of the adult population are either obese or overweight.

In a 1993 study, 14 percent of all deaths in the United States were attributed to activity patterns and diet. Another study linked sedentary lifestyles to 23 percent of deaths from major chronic diseases. For example, physical activity has been shown to reduce the risk of developing or dying from heart disea se, diabetes, colon cancer, and high blood pressure. On average, people who are physically active outlive those who are inactive.

Despite the well-known benefits of physical activity, most adults and many children lead a relatively sedentary lifestyle and are not active enough to achieve these health benefits. A sedentary lifestyle is defined as engaging in no leisure-time physical activity (exercises, sports, physically active hobbies) in a two-week period. Data from the National Health Interview Survey shows that in 1997-98 nearly four in 10 (38.3 percent) adults reported no participation in leisure- time physical activity.

Approximately one-third of persons age 65 or older lead a sedentary lifestyle. Older women are generally less physically active than older men. Fifty-four percent of men and 66 percent of women age 75 and older engage in no leisure-time physical activity. In general, African American older adults are less active than white older adults. In the mid 1990's, 37 percent of white men age 75 and older reported no leisure-time physical activity, compared to 59 percent of African American men age 75 and older; 47 percent of white women age 75 and older reported no leisure-time physical activity, compared to 60 percent of African American women age 75 and older.

Economic Consequences of Inactivity

Physical inactivity and its associated health problems have substantial economic consequences for the U.S. health care system. In the long run, physical inactivity threatens to reverse the decades-long progress that has been made in reducing the morbidity and mortality associated with many chronic conditions such as cardiovascular disease. A physically inactive population is at both medical and financial risk for many chronic diseases and conditions including heart disease, stroke, colon cancer, diabetes, obesity, and osteoporosis.

The increasing prevalence of chronic medical conditions and diseases related to physical inactivity are associated with two types of costs. First, there are health care costs for preventative, diagnostic, and treatment services related to these chronic conditions. These costs may include expenditures for physician visits, pharmaceuticals, ambulance services, rehabilitation services and hospital and nursing home care. In addition, there are other costs associated with the value of lost wages by people unable to work because of illness and disability, as well as the value of future earnings lost by premature death. In 2000, the total cost of overweight and obesity was estimated to be $117 billion. In addition, the total estimated cost from chronic diseases is substantial.

Table 1. National Cost of Illness for Selected Diseases (in billions)

Disease	Cost
Heart Diseases	$183
Cancer	157
Diabetes	100
Arthritis	65

Source: National Institutes of Health, 2000

Individuals suffering from chronic diseases bear a substantial portion of these medical costs. A recent study demonstrated that obese individuals spend approximately 36 percent more than the general population on health services and 77 percent more on medications. Furthermore, the study found that the effects of obesity on health spending were significantly larger than effects of current or past smoking.

The Medicare and Medicaid programs currently spend $84 billion annually on five major chronic conditions that could be significantly improved by increased physical activity, specifically diabetes, heart disease, depression, cancer, and arthritis. Medicare spent $10.4 billion on diabetes treatment and services in 2000 and is estimated to spend $12.7 billion in 2004.

In addition, Medicare spending on heart disease treatment and services has grown from $21.1 billion in 1992 to $34.9 billion in 2000 and is expected to reach $42.8 billion in 2004. Medicare spending on depression treatment and services has grown from $1.3 billion in 1992 to $2.1 billion in 2000 and is estimated to increase to $2.5 billion in 2004.

Medicare spending on cancer treatment and services has grown from $10.3 billion in 1992 to $15.2 billion in 2000 and is expected to increase to $18.5 billion in 2004. Medicare spending on arthritis treatment and services has grown from $3.4 billion in 1992 to $5.8 billion in 2000 and is estimated to be $7.1 billion in 2004.

Since regular physical activity helps prevent disease and promote health, it may actually decrease health care costs. A study performed by researchers at the Centers for Disease Control and Prevention found that physically active people had, on average, lower annual direct medical costs than did inactive people. The same study estimated that increasing regular moderate physical activity among the more than 88 million inactive Americans over the age of 15 years might reduce the annual national direct medical costs by as much as $76.6 billion in 2000 dollars.

Further, it found that physically active people had fewer hospital stays and physician visits and used less medication than physically inactive people. The cost savings were consistent for men and women, for those with and without physical limitations, and even for smokers and nonsmokers.

The researchers concluded that adoption of a population-wide physical activity strategy might produce health care cost savings among most adult age groups.

Employers can benefit too. Workplace physical activity programs can reduce short-term sick leave by six to 32 percent, reduce health care costs by 20 to 55 percent, and increase productivity by 2 to 52 percent. In 1998, 93 percent of employers had programs that fostered employee health, up from 76 percent in 1992, according to Hewitt Associates. Such "wellness" programs typically offer help in smoking cessation, managing stress, prenatal care, nutrition, and fitness.

Physical Activity and Good Physical Health

Participation in regular physical activity— at least 30 minutes of moderate activity on at least five days per week, or 20 minutes of vigorous physical activity at least three times per week—is critical to sustaining good health. Youth should strive for at least one hour of exercise a day. Regular physical activity has beneficial effects on most (if not all) organ systems, and consequently it helps to prevent a broad range of health problems and diseases. People of all ages, both male and female, derive substantial health benefits from physical activity.

Regular physical activity reduces the risk of developing or dying from some of the leading causes of illness in the United States. Regular physical activity improves health in the following ways:

— Reduces the risk of dying prematurely from heart disease and other conditions;

— Reduces the risk of developing diabetes;

— Reduces the risk of developing high blood pressure;

— Reduces blood pressure in people who already have high blood pressure;

— Reduces the risk of developing colon and breast cancer;

— Helps to maintain a healthy weight;

— Helps build and maintain healthy bones, muscles, and joints;

— Helps older adults to become stronger and better able to move about without falling;

— Reduces feelings of depression and anxiety; and

— Promotes psychological well-being.

Regular physical activity is associated with lower mortality rates for both older and younger adults. Even those who are moderately active on a regular basis have lower mortality rates than those who are least active. Regular physical activity leads to cardiovascular fitness, which decreases the risk of cardiovascular disease mortality in general and coronary artery disease mortality in particular. High blood pressure is a major underlying cause of cardiovascular complications and mortality. Regular physical activity can prevent or delay the development of high blood pressure, and reduces blood pressure in persons with hypertension.

Regular physical activity is also important for maintaining muscle strength, joint structure, joint functioning, and bone health. Weight-bearing physical activity is essential for normal skeletal development during childhood and adolescence and for achieving and maintaining peak bone mass in young adults. Among post-menopausal women, exercise, especially muscle strengthening (resistance) activity, may protect against the rapid decline in bone mass. However, data on the effects of exercise on post-menopausal bone loss are not clear-cut and the timing of the intervention (e.g., stage of menopausal transition) can influence the response. Regardless, physical activity including muscle-strengthening exercise appears to protect against falling and fractures among the elderly, probably by increasing muscle strength and balance.

In addition, physical activity may be beneficial for many people with arthritis. Regular physical activity can help improve the lives of young people beyond its effects on physical health. Although research has not been conducted to conclusively demonstrate a direct link between physical activity and improved academic performance, such a link might be expected. Studies have found participation in physical activity increases adolescents' self-esteem and reduces anxiety and stress. Through its effects on mental health, physical activity may help increase students' capacity for learning.

One study found that spending more time in physical education did not have harmful effects on the standardized academic achievement test scores of elementary school students; in fact, there was some evidence that participation in a two-year health-related physical education program had several significant favourable effects on academic achievement. Participation in physical activity and sports can promote social well-being, as well as good physical and mental health, among young people.

Research has shown that students who participate in interscholastic sports are less likely to be regular and heavy smokers or use drugs, and are more likely to stay in school and have good conduct and high academic achievement. Sports and physical activity programs can introduce young people to skills such as teamwork, self-discipline, sportsmanship, leadership, and socialization. Lack of recreational activity, on the other hand, may contribute to making young people more vulnerable to gangs, drugs, or violence.

Physical Activity and Good Mental Health

Regular physical activity reduces morbidity and mortality from mental health disorders. Mental health disorders pose a significant public health burden in the United States and they are a major cause of hospitalization and disability. Mental health disorders cost approximately $148 billion per year. Potentially, increasing physical activity levels in Americans could substantially reduce medical expenditures for mental health conditions.

In adults with affective disorders, physical activity has a beneficial effect on symptoms of depression and anxiety. Animal research suggests that exercise may stimulate the growth of new brain cells that enhance memory and learning—two functions hampered by depression. Clinical studies have demonstrated the feasibility and efficacy of exercise as a treatment for depression in older men and women. Currently, National Institute of Mental Health (NIMH) investigators are conducting research comparing the effectiveness of home-based and supervised aerobic exercise to the use of antidepressants in relieving depression in these groups, and reducing relapse rates.

Other NIMH researchers are studying whether greater exercise levels result in more symptom improvement. Regular physical activity also appears to enhance well-being. The preventive effects of physical activity on mental disorders are less well studied. Some studies suggest physical activity prevents depressive illness. Future research will clarify the extent to which physical activity may actually protect against the development of depression. Regular physical activity may also reduce risk of cognitive decline in older adults, though more research is needed to clarify the mechanism of this possible effect. Among people who suffer from mental illness, physical activity appears to improve the ability to perform activities of daily living.

Depending on the nutrients available to the child within pregnancy and the genetic make up of the child, most healthy babies weight between five and eight pounds. Since the placenta is absent, which previously provided the baby with nutrients, food is required for the metabolic processes and the continued growth of the baby. Its nutrients derive from feeding of liquids by the parents to begin with, as the young baby's digestive system cannot cope with more complex solid foods. This provides the nutrients to begin with for continued growth and development.

Through learning and development, by the end of the first year the baby can feed on solids and perform basic functions such as crawling and walking. The dependence on growth from food from the mother is now switched to the production of hormones in the young child, which now has a developed endocrine system for hormone secretion. At this stage the young child is at a period of accelerated growth, which will continue into early childhood. Depending on the genetics of the baby, the hormones secreted will determine the height of the child in its future years. As a general rule of thumb, the size of the child at 2 years is roughly proportional to its final height barring unusual factors.

Puberty and Adolescence

After early childhood, the child continues to grow steadily in its single figure years up until it becomes a teenager. At this point, puberty begins. Puberty is the point in time where the development of sexual characteristics begin, and will allow these humans to become sexually active and be able to produce gametes for reproduction.

Puberty in Females

On average, most girls tend to reach puberty before boys.

— Oestrogen, a female hormone is secreted by the ovaries, begins to enlarge the breasts which will be later used by the baby to feed on.

— Growth is increased and accelerates over the teenage years as a result of increases in the secretion of growth hormone.

— On average, 20 centimetres are gained in height from puberty

- The menstrual cycle is initiated by the thickening of the uterus caused by the cyclical changes in the presence of oestrogen. This is shed every 28 days and is known as a period. At this point, the female is fertile and able to reproduce

In Males

On average, most boys tend to reach puberty after most girls have developed, though puberty lasts longer

- As with girls, a growth spurt occurs
- Testosterone is produced by the male testes, which initiates the growth spurt, and does so more effectively than oestrogen, making most males on average taller than females
- After secretion of prolonged testosterone, the male shows secondary sex characteristics such as increased bodily hair, deepening of the voice and increased development of muscularity
- The initial secretion of testosterone initiates sperm production, giving the male fertile gametes available for reproduction

By the end of the teenage years puberty ceases and maturity has been reached. At this point, no more true growth occurs (an increase in cell number) and new cells are solely used for regeneration purposes. Women cease to be fertile on average in their 50's where no more eggs are produced by the ovaries. It is interesting to know that a female baby already has over 1 000 000 follicles for eggs to develop in, which decreases to 100 000 by puberty. By the 6th decade of life in the female, this supply will have run out.

Longevity

Better living conditions have led to people in modern societies living to a ripe old age. In light of this, increased study has went into longevity in humans (how long we live) and how we can combat the degenerative nature of aging. Over time our bodies become less efficient, and the homeostasis of an efficient body becomes less able to maintain the favourable conditions. This leads to degeneration of our body, until death.

Internal operations of the human body are explained below.

Food and Digestion

Food is what is required by humans to grow and survive, and provide a 'fuel' for the energy needed in our biological reactions. As opposed to plants that can acquire their food from the soil and sunlight, animals are required to eat foodstuffs in order to create the energy they need to survive. These foods contain many compounds and elements that are useful to our body and our daily functions. This food is entered into the body via the mouth, where enzymes such as lysozyme begin to breakdown the food while it is chewed. When this food is broken down into smaller pieces it can then be swallowed, where it travels down the oesophagus towards the stomach.

The stomach then continues to break down the foodstuff. The stomach at this point is filled with a type of acid that further breaks down the food, until it is in a semi-liquid state. Note that the stomach only acts as a storage point at this stage, until the food slowly passes into the duodenum, which is part of the small intestine. It is here where the food is completely broken down, in the following manner:

— Proteins are broken down into amino acids

— Fats into fatty acids

— Complex sugars into simple sugars

From here, you can see that a complex product (the food you eat) is stripped bare, until the substances that they are broken down to can be used by the body in some way. By breaking down these foodstuffs to their most basic nature, the body can then rebuild these substances as and when required, for example, to create enzymes. The body can then use these substances when they are in demand, such as the raising blood sugar levels in the blood stream so that energy can be created in the cells around the body via respiration. In order for the body to successfully utilise the energy available within the food and use it properly, humans must intake the required amount of nutrients and minerals that our body requires; this can be done by having a balanced diet. A good diet will consist of the right measurement of the following compounds.

— *Vitamins*: Vitamins are required for various chemical reactions in the body. They can be found mostly in dairy products, fruits and vegetables.

— *Proteins*: Proteins are also vitally important as part of a balanced diet. Proteins have many functions such as globular proteins in the body which make enzymes, hormones and antibodies for example, all essential to human existence

— *Carbohydrates*: Carbohydrates are compounds that consist of carbon (carbo-), hydrogen (-hydr-) and oxygen (-ate) atoms. Glucose, the compound that is broken down in the first step of respiration is an example of a carbohydrate, hence the important of carbohydrates in diets.

— *Fats*: Also known as lipids, fats produce twice the amount of energy that carbohydrates are capable of producing, and this is due to the more complex nature of their structure. Their are five different types of lipid, either, triglycerides, phospholipids, glycolipids, steroids and waxes

— *Minerals*: These inorganic substances are required for a variety of reasons in the body. One such example is the requirement of iron, which is present in haemoglobin, in its role of absorbing oxygen from the lungs into the bloodstream.

The right measurement of the above compounds in our daily diet leads to an optimally functioning body, which has all the building blocks it needs to execute cellular processes on a day to day basis. Such a balanced diet also helps combat disease and provide the optimal conditions for our body to operate and grow. If this is not the case, a deficiency in a particular substance can lead to disease.

Balanced diet is essential to a healthy organism. Deficiencies in particular elements can lead to a decline in health, and exhibit symptoms that are not desirable at all. The following information looks at some of these deficiencies and why they happen:

Vitamin A: Vitamin A is essential for night vision and improves effectiveness of the immune system. It can be found in many dairy products, and especially in carrots.

Vitamin B12: This vitamin is essential in the formation of red blood cells and lack of this may cause anaemia.

Vitamin C: Scurvy is caused by a lack of vitamin C in the diet. Vitamin C is essential in the formation of red blood cells, antibodies and a healthy circulatory system. Symptoms of scurvy include bleeding gums and dizziness caused by the deficient blood supply.

Vitamin D: Essential part of the diet required in the absorption of minerals in food, where a lack of vitamin D in the diet leads to a condition called rickets, where softening of the bones cause them to bend from the lack of calcium. Humans have the ability to synthesise vitamin D from sunlight

Vitamin E: Important in preventing the oxidation of fatty acids in cells, and is commonly found in cereals and green vegetables

Vitamin K: Vitamin K is important for the blood clotting process and can be synthesised in the human gut, and found in green vegetables.

A Balanced Diet - Carbohydrates and Fat

Alongside the numerous vitamins that are required as part of a healthy diet, we must also eat food containing a variety of other materials to ensure the day to day running of our body. These building materials are essential to the daily maintenance and growth of a human body, as each are required in the various biological processes that allow us to survive and fight off infection.

Carbohydrates

Carbohydrates are a major source of energy, and contain all the necessary building materials to create *glucose*, a compound that is used in numerous areas across animals and plants. Glucose itself can be found abundantly in sweet fruits, as can fructose, and is the body's method of delivering energy to cells across our body.

Complex sugars, deemed *dissacharides* due to their more complex molecular structure, consist of *monosaccharides* - the fundamental unit of a carbohydrate. Glucose and fructose are examples of monosaccharides. A summary of carbohydrates can be found below:

— *Lactose*: A dissacharide carbohydrate found in milk that is a compound of glucose and galactose.

— *Maltose*: A dissacharide that is found abundantly in germinating grain, as they have a large reserve of starch which can be broken down by the enzyme *-amylase.*

— *Sucrose*: Found in sugar cane, sucrose can be broken down by the enzyme sucrase into fructose and glucose.

— *Glycogen*: The body's preferred storage form of glucose, which can be broken down by glucagon

— *Deoxyribose*: A *pentose* sugar that forms the very genetic material responsible for the creation of all proteins in the body, *DNA*.

— *Ribose*: A pentose sugar.

— *Cellulose*: Is a compound of 4 glucose molecules that are present in the cell walls of plants, and is the most abundant biological material on Earth, due to its tensile nature in acting as a barrier to the outside environment. Cellulose is a type of fibre, which is required in our diet to help digestion.

All in all these malleable compounds that are carbohydrates form an essential part of our diet, with dissacharides and complex carbohydrates acting as building blocks themselves while also being capable of being broken down into a more simple monosaccharide.

Fats

Fats are an important part of a healthy balanced diet, and also act as a means of insulation in our bodies when it is stored under the skin as stored energy, due to them containing twice as much potential energy as carbon. Fats can be broken down into 5 different categories:

— *Triglyceride*: These are formed by glycerol and a set of 3 fatty acids, which together form a triglyceride.

— *Phospholipid*: These consist of a glycerol and phosphate molecule and two fatty acids, which form the cell membrane of cells and responsible for transferring other fats around the body.

— *Wax*: Consisting of alcohols and fatty acid molecules, these types of fat have waterproof qualities and is rimportant consitutent in many species lives.

— *Glycolipid*: Any type of fat that also contains a carbohydrate

— *Steroid*: Cholesterol and cortisone are examples of steroid types of fat.

Fats are an important part of a healthy human diet, due to the compounds they contain as well as their potential energy that is stored in our body's.

Minerals and Proteins

Various mineral in the Earth's crust are required for a healthy balanced diet. These inorganic compounds have various roles in functions of the human body as well as many other species. A summary of the main minerals involved in a balanced diet are outlined below:

— *Iron*: Iron is an essential consitutent of *haemoglobin*, the molecule responsible for transporting oxygen in the bloodstream, and is also a part of cytochrome (an area important in cell respiration) thus is an important mineral to have in our diet.

– *Calcium*: Calcium is required for strong bones and teeth, and also for muscle contraction. Calcium can be found in rich supply in various dairy products such as cheese and milk.

— *Sodium*: Sodium, known more commonly as salt, is required by nerve cells and is also used to produce hydrochloric acid for digestion, which is capable of killing off infections entering the mouth and nose due to its acidic nature.

— *Iodine*: Iodine is used to create thyroxine, a hormone that is partly responsible for controlling metabolic rate in the body.

Proteins

As mentioned in the cell biology tutorial regarding the variety of proteins used in our body, it is essential that our diet contains protein to achieve a healthy balanced diet. They are the building blocks of enzymes, hormones and antibodies, all of which are essential in many biological processes. Proteins consist of *amino acids*, some of these amino acids are deemed *essential amino acids* as they cannot be synthesized from other materials and thus must be part of the diet. Protein is abundant in dairy products, soy beans, meat and cereal; which are all constituents of a healthy balanced diet.

Improving Ryunning Efficiency

Maloiy measured the energy expenditure of Luo women walking with weights, and they exhibited similar parsimony. There are probably over six million Kikuyus within Kenya and almost four million Luo, but Luo and Kikuyu rarely intermarry, and the two groups have dissimilar ancestral bases, so it would be difficult to imagine that both tribes have captured an identical super gene, or even some set of super genes. Fortunately, Heglund has a different explanation. In research which followed the initial explorations of Kikuyu economy, Heglund and his friend Giovanni Cavagna of the University of Milan asked two women to carry loads Kikuyu style (with straps on their heads), two to carry loads Luo style (with weights directly on their head), and one to use both styles of support.

For comparison, six male and six female Europeans carried similar loads in backpacks. All individuals walked across a force platform mounted at ground level in the middle of a walkway with and without the loads, and gravitational potential energy and kinetic energy were measured from the measured forces. Heglund and colleagues focused closely on the conversion of kinetic energy to potential energy and back again during the various walks. Interestingly, the ability to convert energy back and forth without losing it increased with increasing load in the African women, explaining why they could carry extra weight without increasing their basic energy expenditure.

Under normal circumstances, walking individuals can preserve about 65% of their total energy of movement per step, but the African women could hold onto over 80% of their movement energy as their loads increased to 20% of body weight. How did the women manage to be so efficient? According to the researchers, the answer can be found in what happens during footstrike. As individuals move through the 'top' of one stride (remember the pendulum analogy; the top of the walking stride is when the centre of mass reaches its greatest height and potential energy attains its maximum) and start to fall into the next step, most pause for a few milliseconds before beginning to fall.

Muscles in the legs are contracting and fighting the fall, trying to preserve balance. This decelerates the body (causing a loss of energy during the potential-kinetic transfer) and, of course, increases energy expenditure. By contrast, the Kenyan women shorten or eliminate the pause at the top of the stride. Thus, there is no added deceleration, no loss of potential energy, and no unnecessary increase in energy expenditure associated with muscular contractions (since the muscles aren't trying to exert a braking effect at the stride's top). The Kenyan women are, in effect, more perfect pendulums. In effect, the Kenyan women eliminate braking actions during the footstrike portion of gait and thus improve their efficiency.

Runners can do the same thing. If they take off the brakes and eliminate the pause during footstrike, they will be better able to preserve potential and kinetic energy, and our energy cost - expressed as either calories or millilitres of oxygen per minute - will be lower. Since they will be operating at a lower percentage of VO2max, their efforts will feel easier, and so they can step up their training and race paces. But how do they actually take the brakes off?

Two factors must be at work: first, our nervous systems must be highly reactive, so that muscular actions which inhibit forward propulsion can be tightly controlled from the moment of impact, and muscular actions which boost propulsion can be instigated without hesitation. Second, our movements must be well coordinated, so that there is no need to spend extra time (and energy) restoring the body's equilibrium position. Footstrike must be an explosive time, not a period in which weakly controlled joint movements must be corrected prior to toe-off, or in which the leg muscles 'throw on the brakes'. What they want to achieve is speed and control.

Exercises that will improve that all-important footstrike. To dramatically enhance speed, abbreviate the duration of footstrike, and decrease energy wastage during the footstrike portion of walking and running, carry out the following routine several times a week.

1. *Springy jogging*: jog along with very springy, short steps, landing on the mid-foot area with each contact and springing upwards after impact. As you move along, your ankles should act like coiled springs, compressing slightly with each mid-foot landing and then recoiling quickly - causing you to bound upwards and forwards. Move along for one minute with quick little spring-like strides, alternating right and left feet as you would during regular running. After this minute is completed, jog in your regular manner for about 10secs, and then 'spring-jog' for about 20m, alternating three consecutive spring-like contacts with your right foot with three contacts with the left (eg three hops on your right foot, three hops on your left, three more on your right, etc, until you have travelled about 20m). Jog in your usual manner for 10secs again, and then spring-hop along for 20m on your right foot only, before shifting over to 20m on the left foot alone (making certain that you land in the mid-foot area with each ground contact).

2. *One-leg hops on the spot*: two sets of 40secs on each leg. Stand in a relaxed position, with your full body weight supported on your left foot only. Lift your left heel slightly, so that the force of body weight is passing through the ball of the left foot (your right knee is flexed so that your right knee is off the ground). Then, hop rapidly on your left foot at a cadence of 2.5 to 3 hops per second (25 to 30 foot contacts per 10secs) for the prescribed time period, while maintaining relaxed, upright posture. Your left foot should strike the ground in the area of the mid-foot and spring upwards rapidly, as though it were contacting a very hot burner on a stove. Your hips should remain fairly level as you do this; try to minimise vertical displacement of the upper body.

3. *'Box-hop' with 'sticks'*: for 60secs on your right foot, rest for a few seconds, and then shift over to 60secs of box hopping on your left foot. After resting for a moment, repeat with each foot. The box utilised for this exercise should be sturdy and about six inches in height. To perform the exercise, stand about two metres away from the box, and then hop forward quickly towards the box on one foot only. As you near the box, hop up onto the box surface (continuing to hop on only the chosen foot), and then hop quickly off the 'far' side of the box. When you land on the other side, hop forward explosively, ie with as little ground-contact time as possible. In this explosive hop, try to avoid significant vertical oscillation of your centre of mass; you are trying for length, not height. When you land from this explosive hop, continue hopping on the same foot for four more hops, and when your foot touches down after the fourth hop, 'stick' your position, ie stop movement completely while remaining relaxed and nicely balanced on your single foot. Jog back to the starting point on both feet, and then continue the exercise on the chosen foot until the time limit is up. Following a short rest, do the hopping routine on the other foot.

4. *High-knee explosions*: complete 10 with your right leg, rest for a few seconds, and repeat with your left leg. To carry these out, stand with erect but relaxed posture with your full body weight supported on your right foot. Begin by jumping very lightly on the spot on your right foot only, but then suddenly - while maintaining fairly erect posture - jump vertically while swinging your right knee up towards your chest (your left arm should swing forward as your right knee comes up). Land back on your right foot in a relaxed and resilient manner, jump lightly for a few moments, and repeat nine more times, before resting briefly and continuing the pattern on your left leg.

5. *Shane's in-place accelerations*: to carry these out, stand with erect but relaxed posture with your feet directly below your shoulders. Begin by simply jogging on the spot, but

then - when you feel ready - begin to dramatically increase your in-place 'stride rate', building up fairly quickly to as rapid a rate of striding as you can sustain (remember that you are not moving forward to any significant degree). Keep your feet close to the ground as you do this; you're not shooting for high knee lift but rather for dramatically minimised foot-contact times. Maintain erect but relaxed posture. As you accelerate up to 'top speed', it sometimes helps to turn your legs slightly outwards at the hips. Perform 3 x 20secs.

To minimise the risk of injury, at least at first, please make sure that all of these activities are completed on a 'forgiving' surface (soft dirt, grass, cushioned artificial turf, or wooden gym floor). This group of quicksilver exercises will, of course, enhance the reactivity of your nervous system and thus help to minimise footstrike time. Naturally, strength and coordination of the weight-bearing leg are also needed to ensure that energy will not be wasted correcting non-optimal leg and body movements associated with footstrike. As mentioned, the overall idea is to create quick-to-act legs which channel all available energy towards forward propulsion, without the need to correct anti-propulsive movements. Towards that end, the following exercise strengthens the legs tremendously and improves balance and coordination to a close-to-maximal extent.

Partial Squats: one set per leg. Stand with your left foot directly under your left shoulder, keeping your left knee just slightly flexed and maintaining relaxed, fairly erect posture. Hold the barbell (initially with no weights attached) so that it rests on the top-back of your shoulders just behind your neck; you may incline your upper body just slightly forward for balance. Most of your body weight should be directed through the heel to mid-portion of your left foot. Your right leg should be flexed at the knee so that the foot is not touching the ground at all - your right foot is literally suspended in air (although, you may occasionally need to 'spot-touch' the floor for balance with your trailing leg). From this position, if you were carrying out a traditional one-leg squat you would ordinarily bend your left leg at the knee and lower your body until your left knee reached an angle of about 90 degrees between the backs of your thigh and lower leg (usually at this point your thigh would be almost parallel with the ground).

However, for the partial squat you should just go down about half-way - so that the angle between the back of your thigh and lower leg is just 135 degrees or so. Then return to the starting position, maintaining upright posture with your trunk. That's one rep! So far so good - but you have lots more work to do! Continue in the manner described above until you have completed 10 reps (10 partial squats). Then - without resting - descend into the 11th partial squat, but instead of rising back up hold the partial-squat position (the 135-degree position) for 10 full seconds. We'll call your body alignment during this 10-second period the 'static-hold' position.

After completing 10secs in the static-hold position, immediately - without resting - rattle off 10 more reps, maintain the static hold on the 11th rep for 10secs again, hit 10 more reps, and then hold statically for 10 more seconds on the 11th rep. That's one set! To summarise, a set proceeds as follows (with no recovery at all within the set):

1. 10 partial squats
2. 10 seconds of holding your leg and body in the down position
3. 10 partial squats
4. 10 seconds of holding
5. 10 partial squats
6. 10 seconds of holding

If you complete these six exercises two to three times a week and emphasise intensity of effort in your regular walking or running training, you will soon develop springy, explosive legs which refuse to dawdle during footstrike and put all available energy into moving you forward. Soon you'll be moving more efficiently, like a Kikuyu woman, even if you are a white male.

The good news is that such efficient movements will make you a truly faster runner, whether you are a soccer player, rugby enthusiast, basketball player, cricketer, or marathon runner.

Physical Activity: AKey to Maintaining Energy Balance and a Healthy Weight

Regular physical activity along with a nutritious diet is key to maintaining a healthy weight. In order to maintain a healthy weight, there must be a balance between calories consumed and calories expended through metabolic and physical activity. Although overweight and obesity are caused by many factors, in most individuals, weight gain results from a combination of excess calorie consumption and inadequate physical activity.

Even though a large portion of a person's total caloric requirement is used for basal metabolism and processing food, an individual's various physical activities may account for as much as 15 to 40 percent of the calories he or she burns each day. While vigorous exercise uses calories at a higher rate, any physical activity will burn calories. For example, a 140-pound person can burn 175 calories in 30 minutes of moderate bicycling, and 322 calories in 30 minutes of moderate jogging. The same person can also burn 105 calories by vacuuming or raking leaves for the same amount of time.

Overweight and Obesity

As a result of lifestyle and dietary changes, overweight and obesity have reached epidemic proportions in the United States. The Body Mass Index (BMI) is the most commonly used measure to define overweight and obesity. BMI is a measure of weight in relation to height. BMI is calculated as weight in pounds divided by the square of the height in inches, multiplied by 703.

According to the National Institutes of Health Clinical Guidelines, overweight in adults is defined as a BMI between

25 lbs/in^2 to 29.9 lbs/in^2; and obesity in adults is identified by a BMI of 30 lbs/in^2 or greater. These definitions are based on evidence that suggests that health risks are greater at or above a BMI of 25 lbs/in^2 compared to those at a BMI below that level. The risk of premature death increases with an increasing BMI. This increase in mortality tends to be modest until a BMI of 30 lbs/in^2 is reached.

Overweight and obesity are increasing in both genders and among all population groups. In 1999, an estimated 61 percent of adults in the U.S. were overweight or obese; this contrasts with the late 1970s, when an estimated 47 percent of adults were overweight or obese.

Among women, the prevalence of overweight and obesity generally is higher in women who are members of racial and ethnic minority populations than in non-Hispanic white women. Among men, Mexican Americans have a higher prevalence of overweight and obesity than non-Hispanic whites or non-Hispanic blacks. For non-Hispanic men, the prevalence of overweight and obesity among whites is slightly greater than among blacks.

Disparities in prevalence of overweight and obesity also exist based on socioeconomic status. For all racial and ethnic groups combined, women of lower socioeconomic status (income $\leq$130 percent of the poverty threshold) are approximately 50 percent more likely to be obese than those with higher socioeconomic status (income > 130 percent of the poverty threshold). Men are about equally likely to be obese whether they are in a low or high socioeconomic group.

The overweight and obesity epidemic is not limited to adults. What is particularly alarming is that the percentage of young people who are overweight has almost doubled in the last 20 years for children aged 6-11 and almost tripled for adolescents aged 12-19. In children and adolescents, overweight has been defined as a sex- and age- specific BMI at or above the 95th percentile for a reference population.

Epidemiological studies show an increase in mortality associated with overweight and obesity. Approximately 300,000 deaths a year in this country are currently associated with overweight and obesity. Morbidity from obesity may be as great as from poverty, smoking, or problem drinking. Overweight and obesity are associated with an increased risk for developing various medical conditions including cardiovascular disease, certain cancers (endometrial, colon, postmenopausal breast, kidney, and esophageal), high blood pressure, arthritis-related disabilities and type 2 diabetes.

Table 2. Health risks associated with obesity

Obesity is Associated with an Increased Risk of:	
- premature death	- high blood cholesterol
- type 2 diabetes	- complications of pregnancy
- heart disease	- menstrual irregularities
- stroke	- hirsutism (presence of excess body and facial hair)
- hypertension	
- gallbladder disease	- stress incontinence (urine leakge caused by weak pelvic-floor muscles)
- osteoarthritis (degeneration of cartilage and bone in joints)	
- sleep apnea	- increased surgical risk
- asthma	- psychological disorders such as depression
- breathing problems	
- cancer (endometrial, colon, kidney, esophageal, and postmenopausal breast cancer)	- psychological difficulties due to social stigmatization

Source: Surgeon General's Call to Action to Prevent and Decrease Overweight and Obesity, 2001

It is also important for individuals who are currently at a healthy weight to strive to maintain it since both modest and large weight gains are associated with significantly increased risk of disease. For example, a weight gain of 11 to 18 pounds increases a person's risk for developing type 2 diabetes to twice that of individuals who have not gained weight, while those who gain 44 pounds or more have four times the risk of type 2 diabetes.

Recent research studies have shown that a gain of 10 to 20 pounds resulted in an increased risk of coronary heart disease (which can result in nonfatal heart attacks and death) of 1.25 times in women and 1.6 times in men. In these studies, weight increases of 22 pounds in men and 44 pounds in women resulted in a increased coronary heart disease risk of 1.75 and 2.65, respectively. In one study among women with a BMI of 34 or greater, the risk of developing endometrial cancer was increased by more than 6 times. Overweight and obesity are also known to exacerbate many chronic conditions such as hypertension and elevated cholesterol. Overweight and obese individuals also may suffer from social stigmatization, discrimination, and poor body image.

Although obesity-associated morbidities occur most frequently in adults, important consequences of excess weight as well as antecedents of adult disease occur in overweight children and adolescents. Overweight children and adolescents are more likely to become overweight or obese adults. As the prevalence of overweight and obesity increases in children and adolescents, type 2 diabetes, high blood lipids, and hypertension as well as early maturation and orthopedic problems are occurring with increased frequency. A common consequence of childhood overweight is psychosocial—specifically discrimination.

Call to Action

Because physical inactivity is a risk factor for many diseases and conditions, making physical activity an integral part of daily life is crucial. Physical activity need not be strenuous to be beneficial. People of all ages benefit from moderate physical activity, such as 30 minutes of walking five or more times a week. In addition, physical activity does not need to be sustained for long periods of time in order to provide health benefits. Repeated shorter bursts of moderate-intensity activity also yield health benefits. In other words, walking in two 15-minute segments or three 10-minute segments is beneficial.

Clearly, the goal of a more active population will be a challenge, requiring a commitment to change on the part of individuals, families, work places, and communities. Both the public and private sectors will need to band together to promote more healthy habits for those of all ages. Encouraging more activity can be as simple as establishing walking programs at schools, worksites and in the community. Some communities have an existing infrastructure that supports physical activity, such as sidewalks and bicycle trails, and work sites, schools, and shopping areas in close proximity to residential areas.

In many other areas, such community amenities need to be developed to foster walking, cycling, and other types of exercise as a regular part of daily activity. Schools provide many opportunities to engage children in physical activity as well as healthy eating. For adults, worksites provide opportunities to reinforce the adoption and maintenance of healthy lifestyle behaviours. Perhaps the most important change, however, is at the individual and family level. Each person must understand the value of physical activity for his or her health and well-being and commit to a lifestyle that is truly active.

Vision of Physical Education Development

The ultimate goal of comprehensive health and physical education programs is to aid students in achieving their fullest potentiai through the acquisition of knowledge and skills necessary to attain healthy levels of well being and to maintain active lifestyles throughout the lifespan. The foundation of all health and physical education programs is the interrelationship of physical, mental, emotional, and social health and well being. Learners will establish a solid foundation for maintaining healthy, active, and productive lives. Learners must develop movement skills leading toward competency in self-selected activity, healthy levels of fitness, and cooperative interaction skills needed for successful participation in an active lifestyle.

Teamwork and cooperative skills are used to work effectively with others, set individual and group goals, solve problems, and enhance the quality of interpersonal relationships. Learners will communicate and work in ways that promote and maintain dignity and respect for themselves and others. Through mastery of knowledge, skills, and behaviors essential to healthy living, learners will accept responsibility and consequences for personal decisions and behaviors. The result of persons leading healthy and physically active lifestyles is seen in an increased capacity for effective work, positive behavioral choices, and increased academic success.

Physical Development and Health: Goal Statement

— Goal 19 – Acquire movement skills and understand concepts needed to engage in health enhancing physical activity. A physically educated person demonstrates sufficient skill in movement, uses effective game and performance strategies, follows rules for activities, and is able to develop a means for enhancing personal movement efficiency, culminating in the ability to perform proficiently in at least one selected activity. Students must learn basic skills, rules, and strategies for a variety of team sports, individual sports, lifetime activities, and creative movements in order to select personally fulfilling activities for a lifetime. Students must also understand mechanical analysis of skill execution to understand how skills are developed so they can learn new skills later in life or can modify skills to meet changes resulting from aging or injury.

— Goal 20 – Achieve and maintain a health-enhancing level of physical fitness based upon continual self-assessment.

A physically educated person develops and maintains a healthy zone of fitness. The fitness level is periodically assessed and is maintained at sufficient levels to allow the learner to participate completely in chosen activities and reflects a low risk for diseases associated with unhealthy and inactive lifestyle choices. Students must understand how to assess fitness in each health-related component, must be able to select activities that contribute to improvement or maintenance in each fitness component, and must have the ability to plan a fit and healthy lifestyle across the age span.

— Goal 21 – Develop team-building skills by working with others through physical activity. A physically educated person can apply principles of teamwork within physical activity to group activities within the family, community, or workplace. Students must display acceptable levels of individual responsibility, cooperation, and respect for self and others in everyday life experiences. Students must learn to problem solve, make decisions, accept responsibilities for consequences, work with decisions made by others, develop and follow procedures, and determine when to compete or cooperate.

— Goal 22 – Understand principles of health promotion and the prevention and treatment of illness and injury. A health-literate person understands interrelationships among physical, mental, emotional, and social well-being and the prevention of illness and disease. From an early age, a health-literate person recognizes that achieving and maintaining personal health is dependent on their ability to positively impact their physical, mental, emotional, and social well-being. By adopting behaviors and making choices that minimize illness and promote health, a health-literate person will increase the chances of not only living a long life, but also, a productive life.

— Goal 23 – Understand human body systems and factors that influence growth and development. A health-literate person will understand human anatomy, physiology, and the stages of growth and development throughout the life cycle. They will understand how growth and development are impacted by factors such as: age, heredity, nutrition, physical activity, illness, stress, substances, and the environment. A health-literate person will understand how systems of the human body work together and impact each other. They will know how behaviors and/or choices affect the functioning of the systems.

— Goal 24 – Promote and enhance health and well-being through the use of effective communication and decision-making skills. A health-literate person makes knowledgeable and informed decisions as well as accepts responsibility for the consequences of these decisions. A health-literate person is an effective communicator who is able to communicate beliefs, information, opinions, and emotions necessary to strengthen relationships as well as avoid conflict. When communicating, a health-literate person will show respect, sensitivity and tolerance for the beliefs, opinions, and feelings of others. These communication skills will allow students to grow and mature into responsible, reasonable, and caring adults.

The goal of physical education is to use physical activity and sports to enhance the mental, physical, and social growth of young women. Physical education is based on health-related fitness, character development, and teamwork skills. The long-term goal of P.E. is to increase cardiovascular endurance, flexibility, and muscular strength.

2

Factors Affecting Growth and Development

Today, patterns of family living, changing demands in the workplace, the aging society, the role of technology in the transformation of active lifestyles, and the impact of health care costs are among the major issues we face. If our children are to prosper in the future and in a world of continual change, we must critically examine the depth and breadth of their preparation to become healthy and productive citizens, parents, and consumers.

The disciplines of health, physical education, and family and consumer sciences enable students to become competent and confident adults. These disciplines focus on the development of the whole person. Through active participation and hands-on-learning, students develop a better understanding of themselves and their world that enables them to analyse their academic, physical, social, and emotional well-being. By studying these disciplines, students set goals, make informed decisions, and learn to balance the demands of daily living.

Learning Standards of Physical Education

There are three learning standards for the disciplines of health, physical education, and family and consumer sciences. These standards share a common focus of giving students knowledge to make wise choices about their own well-being, the skills to follow through on those choices, and the civic values to accept and carry out their responsibilities as members of society. Through these disciplines, students come to understand that they have the responsibility and capability for taking care of themselves and their environments. This concept of responsibility and ability is the cornerstone to all three disciplines.

Standard 1: Personal Health and Fitness

Students will have the necessary knowledge and skills to establish and maintain physical fitness, participate in physical activity, and maintain personal health.

Through their education, students should develop the ability to take care of themselves. Such ability requires the acquisition of a significant body of knowledge. For example, planning a balanced diet requires knowledge of the food pyramid and its contribution to good health; designing a personal exercise program depends on an understanding of such terms as "target heart rate" and "aerobic training"; successfully participating in workplace, community, and family demands skills ranging from balancing a checkbook to recycling household materials appropriately. Physical fitness, exercise, nutrition, dangers of substance abuse, emotional health, and survival skills are areas of study related to this standard.

Standard 2: A Safe and Healthy Environment

Students will acquire the knowledge and ability necessary to create and maintain a safe and healthy environment.

Students must know how to take care of those who depend on them (e.g., younger siblings, children for whom they babysit, their own future children, injured companions, the elderly, or ill relatives) and how to maintain safe and healthy conditions in their environment. The areas of study that will help a student meet this standard are safety, first aid, community health, sports and recreation, parenting and care giving, and family and human development.

Standard 3: Resource Management

Students will understand and be able to manage their personal and community resources. This standard requires the ability to take stock of one's various resources and plan accordingly. The areas of study that will help a student meet this standard include planning of physical and health care; consumer and financial management; clothing and design; housing and environment repair and maintenance; and food preparation and preservation.

Teach Health Education, Physical Education, and Family and Consumer Sciences?

Each discipline makes a unique contribution to the development of the whole child. Together the disciplines mutually reinforce a comprehensive approach to personal well-being and managing one's life. They promote a responsible perspective for personal, family, and community life as well as career development. The benefits for students are enhanced when professional staff in these three disciplines coordinate their efforts to provide a sequential, integrated course of study

Benefits of health Education

— prepares students to meet the challenges of healthy living

— focuses on the whole person

— requires collaboration of home, school, and community

— provides knowledge and skills to enable individuals to make responsible and informed decisions and adapt and maintain healthy behaviours

— prepares students to obtain, interpret, and understand basic health information and services
— prepares students to meet the challenge of healthy living
— focuses on all aspects of health and well-being-physical, mental, emotional, and social
— provides knowledge, motivation, and skills.

Benefits of Physical Education

— counteracts major risk factors of heart disease (high blood pressure, obesity, and sedentary lifestyles)
— improves muscular strength, flexibility, and endurance
— improves self-confidence, self-esteem, and self-control
— teaches children to follow rules and established procedures
— develops motor/movement skills
— helps release tension and anxiety, and increases bone density
— promotes a positive, lifelong attitude toward physical activity
— provides opportunities for students to acquire and demonstrate social skills, cooperative skills, diligent work habits, respect for others, and integrity.

Health education instills in students the knowledge and skills needed to examine alternatives and make responsible health-related decisions. Drawing on knowledge from the biological, environmental, psychological, social, physical, and medical sciences, health education helps students learn to prevent and manage health problems.

— *Human Growth and Development:* Knowing the human body and understanding the characteristics and natural progression of development in the life cycle for taking actions that promote health at each developmental stage.

— *Nutrition*: Understanding the role of nutrition in the promotion and maintenance of health for establishing sound nutritional practices.

— *Family Life*: Appreciating the role of the family in society in preparing each member for the responsibilities of family membership and adulthood, including marriage and parenthood.

— *Alcohol, Tobacco, and Other Drug Substances*: Understanding the factors involved in using drug substances appropriately and preventing abuse.

— *Safety, First Aid, and Survival*: Recognizing how safe environments promote health and well-being and learning procedures to reduce safety risks and respond effectively in emergencies.

— *Community Health*: Understanding the importance of developing health services responsive to present and projected community needs and for becoming a contributor to the health of the community.

— *Environmental Health*: Recognizing that environmental factors have a direct effect on the health of the individual and of society and for taking actions that protect and improve the environment.

— *Diseases and Disorders*: Understanding diseases and disorders and taking actions to prevent or to limit their development.

— *Consumer Health*: Understanding the factors involved in consumer health for making wise decisions in selecting and using health information, products, and services.

— *Emotional Health*: Recognizing the relationships among emotional reactions, social relationships, and health for establishing patterns of behaviour that promote emotional health and sound interpersonal relationships.

— *Healthful Life Styles*: Appreciating the need for responsibility and planning for developing and maintaining a healthful life style.

Comprehensive School Health: What Is It?

Comprehensive school health is defined as:

A planned and coordinated school-based program designed to enhance child and adolescent health and is comprised of eight components:

— healthful school environment

— health services

— health education

— physical education

— counseling and psychological and social services

— nutrition services

— parent and community involvement

— health promotion for staff.

Comprehensive school health is delivered by a set of integrated, planned, and sequential school-affiliated strategies, activities, and services designed to promote the physical, emotional, social, and educational development of students.

Comprehensive school health embraces a broad mission:

To promote collaboration between family and community resources so that all in the school and the community share responsibility for promoting good health.

Comprehensive school health represents an expansion of traditional elements of school health:

— health education

— health services

— a healthy school environment.

Comprehensive school health programs:

— involve and support families

— are determined by community needs, resources, requirements, and standards

— are coordinated by a multidisciplinary team

— are accountable to the community

— improve health from childhood on

— reduce health care costs.

Community school health is recognized by government and educators as a promising approach to achieving the nation's health and education goals.

Physical education is based upon the acquisition of knowledge and skills as a foundation for engaging in physical activity. However, the mere acquisition of knowledge and skills is not enough. The mission of physical education is to enable all students to sustain regular, lifelong physical activity as a foundation for a healthy, productive, and fulfilling life. Physical education is a sequential educational program based on physical activities undertaken in an active, caring, supportive, and non-threatening atmosphere in which every student is challenged and successful. Students with disabilities are provided with a learning environment that is modified, when necessary, to allow for maximum participation.

As the result of a quality K-12 physical education experience, students will:

— acquire the knowledge and skill necessary to perform basic motor and manipulative skills and attain competency in a variety of physical activities and proficiency in a few select complex motor and sport activities

— design personal fitness programs to achieve and maintain physical fitness

— know the benefits of engaging in regular physical activity

— demonstrate responsible personal and social behaviour while engaged in physical activity

— understand that participation in physical activity promotes inclusion of diverse people and understanding of differences among people

— understand that physical activity provides the opportunity for enjoyment, challenge, self-expression, and communication

— participate regularly in health-enhancing physical activities.

Areas of Study in Physical Education

Motor/Movement Skill Development

Motor/movement skills are basic to the actions of daily life and of games, sports, and recreational activities. Teaching movement skills is grounded in the disciplines of anatomy, motor learning, biomechanics, and kinesiology. Through a developmentally appropriate progression of activities, based on a strong foundation of motor, nonlocomotor, and manipulative skills, all students regardless of ability can engage in physical activity with competence and confidence.

In order to participate in a variety of physical activities throughout life, the student needs to master a number of motor/movement skills at a very young age. All students need to demonstrate competency in a wide variety of activities and mastery in a few selected ones, preferably those that can be enjoyed throughout adult life.

Personal Fitness/Wellness

Personal fitness/wellness, a focus of study that has become well established in the past 20 years, is based on a balance of behaviours and actions that enhance good health, quality of life, and well-being. This balance extends beyond physical fitness to disease prevention, stress management, substance abuse control, nutrition, and safety. Teaching physical fitness is grounded in concepts from physiology and physiology of exercise.

In physical education, physical fitness can be taught as a unit of instruction or in the context of physical activities. Students gain an understanding of the importance of developing and maintaining optimum fitness in the areas of cardiorespiratory endurance, flexibility, muscular strength and endurance and body composition. Participating in physical activity is one of the best ways of developing positive self-esteem. It is an opportunity for students of all abilities to engage in a variety of group activities to increase their levels of physical fitness.

Personal Living Skills

Physical education provides a unique opportunity for students to engage in activities that foster the growth of personal living skills. There are three primary categories that make up personal living skills. They include self-reliance, social skills, and personal management skills. The schematic that follows highlights the specific skills encompassed in these categories.

An athlete's ability to acquire, process, store, and recall the intricate phases of motor skill development is crucial to performance. However, it might help to have a better understanding of an athlete's physical limitations when determining what can and cannot be done from the perspectives of skill execution and coaching strategy, then marrying this knowledge with a game plan for addressing his/her special needs. Some of these genetic variables can be positively altered with training, while others are relatively immune to change. For instance, progressive strength training can induce muscular hypertrophy (size), regardless of predominant muscle fiber (slow, intermediate, or fast twitch) composition. However, no type of training can change muscle origin and insertion points, which are cardinal to leverage advantages/disadvantages in joint compartments.

Let's take a closer look at just a short list of genetic factors that play a significant role in the rate and level of physical improvements over time, irrespective of training methodology.

Somatotype

Commonly referred to as "body type," somatotype refers to an individual's body composition; i.e., lean mass (bone, connective tissue, muscle, etc.) to fat mass ratio, as well as other features that are determined by bone length and/or girth. There are three basic somatotype classifications:

1. Mesomorph – Typical characteristics include large, toned muscles with a wide chest, broad shoulders, thick hips, and a relatively slim waistline. True mesomorphs have a very high lean weight composition, and are traditionally capable of demonstrating very good strength and power indices.
2. Ectomorph — Identified by overall slender physique, often with long limbs, low body fat, and minimal muscular girth. Even though the ectomorph may lack long, thick muscle bellies, it is possible that he/she exhibits some prominent muscular definition, due to a very low body fat composition. However, the aforementioned combinations — when discounting other neurological and fiber type contributions — do not lend themselves to a fast rate of muscular development, or the ability to demonstrate great strength or power.
3. Endomorph – This individual is identified by carrying a high percentage of body fat, round features, and very little, if any, muscle tonus (definition). Endomorphs usually have difficulty with activities involving speed, quickness, and agility, though they may fare well in certain tests of strength and power. Their affinity for higher body fat does not necessarily indicate a lack of muscle tissue and its properties, though the muscle is sometimes "hidden" by subcutaneous fat.

The caveat to all of this is that nothing is sacrosanct when it comes to somatotyping. There are certainly exceptions to every description mentioned above, and I'm sure that you've seen athletes who defy science with their athleticism. In other words, their performance doesn't match their appearance as they step off the bus! Truth is, the majority of both the general and athletic populations have characteristics from all three somatotype classifications. Obviously, those that have been blessed with more mesomorphic traits possess greater potential in most athletic endeavors.

Muscle Fiber Type Percentages

If you were to take a cross section of muscle tissue from anywhere in the muscular system and study it for fiber composition, you would be presented with a spectrum of fiber types. Although the conglomeration of fiber types and their functions are much more involved and debated than this elementary description, we will simply refer to them as either slow twitch or fast twitch muscle fibers. Here is a brief description of both fiber types:

— Slow twitch fibers (ST) — They are relatively small in size, slower in contraction, and produce less overall force when compared to fast twitch fibers. However, they have higher endurance capabilities than their fast twitch counterparts. The common misconception engulfing ST fibers is that they are solely responsible for "slow' movements. Actually, ST fibers can generate relatively fast movement speeds, as long as the force requirements are within their capabilities.

— Fast twitch fiber (FT) — These are larger, more powerful fibers that are called upon when the force requirements exceed the qualifications of ST fibers. The physiological makeup of FT fibers enables them to contract with higher speed and respond to elevated force requirements. FT fibers also have a favourable predisposition for hypertrophy (size increase) through progressive strength training, which only magnifies their potential.

Athletes who are bestowed with a high percentage of FT fibers in the muscle groups used for sport skills where rapid, powerful movements are a requisite (e.g., sprinters, competitive weightlifters, football/ basketball/ ice hockey players, baseball pitchers, shot putters/discuss/javelin throwers, etc.) will have a better chance of excelling in those skills. Now, how do know what the predominate fiber type is in a given muscle or group of muscles without being invasive via a muscle biopsy? That's a tough call, but the really gifted ones are not that hard to pick out. They are the extremely strong, fast, quick, explosive athletes – and odds are they were that way long before any formal training.

The next time you pass a playground full of youngsters playing stickball, basketball, dodge ball, or just hanging around on the monkey bars, stop and observe for a few minutes. You will be able to identify the "fast twitch" kids very easily.

Connective Tissue Issues

A tendon is a strong, fibrous connective tissue that connects muscle to bone. The muscle belly is positioned between the two points of attachment, known as the origin (the "immovable" attachment), and the insertion (the "movable" attachment). A long muscle belly in relation to the tendon will augment strength potential. Quite simply, this is an indication that there is probably more cross section of muscle tissue available for development through training. With the possible exceptions of the calves, palm side of the forearm, biceps, and triceps, muscle belly length is difficult to note. Those athletes whose entire skeletal system seems to be covered with thick, prominent muscle tissue, are most likely the ones who have the long muscle bellies with relatively short tendons.

Tendon Insertion Points

Another paramount factor regarding connective tissue is the tendon point of attachment on the bone. The farther away the tendon attaches the muscle from the axis of rotation, the greater the biomechanical leverage. This is one reason why you will see some of those very thin athletes – who you thought were weak — perform surprisingly well in various feats of strength.

Bone Length

Individuals with shorter bones (the body's "levers") may also demonstrate greater leverage in certain athletic skills. This holds especially true for weightlifting and other tasks requiring pushing and/or pulling movements. Here's the rationale supporting this: A person with longer arms and legs is performing more work in these tasks relative to the person with shorter limbs. In other words, they are pushing/pulling the weight over a greater distance, which requires more overall work.

This is one reason why you will not find an inordinate number of world-class competitive weightlifters who have extremely long limbs in proportion to the rest of their bodies. Conversely, many great collegiate and NFL offensive linemen have quite extensive "wing spans," which gives them a leverage advantage when keeping pass rushers in check.

Final Rep

There are many other inherited physical markers that can have a profound effect on an athlete's progress. One such marker that can tie-in many of the aforementioned traits into a cohesive, well-oiled physical machine is neurological efficiency. This is the ability of the central nervous system (CNS) to call on muscle fibers at a quick rate and to a high level. The greater the percentage of fibers activated in the least amount of time usually results in the initiation, execution, and completion of skills with great speed and strength.

Neurological efficiency is thought by many to be the "difference maker" in separating truly great athletes from the rest.

Hormonal influences (testosterone and human growth hormone) also play a key role, though endogenous (normal) secretion and stimulation of these hormones through exercise are, again, totally dependent on individually inherited capabilities. These are the body's naturally occurring "anabolic," or muscle building, hormones.

Athletes, coaches, and parents must be cognizant of the fact that there is an extensive gap between creating and facilitating physical improvement. The best that we can hope to accomplish through our myriad training procedures is to facilitate the growth and development of inherited raw material.

Factors Affecting Strength

Many people feel that they must be doing something wrong because they aren't getting the same results as another person. It's important to realize that there are six primary factors affecting every individual's ability to achieve strength and muscle development, and we have little or no control over most of them.

Type of Muscle Fiber

One of the most influential factors is muscle fiber type. We have two basic types of muscle fibers, often referred to as "slow twitch" and "fast twitch." Slow twitch muscle fibers are best used for cardiovascular (aerobic) activities. They produce small levels of force for long periods of time and thus are better suited for endurance activities. Fast twitch fibers are best used for anaerobic activities. They produce high levels of force for short periods of time and are best suited for power activities such as weightlifting.

Most men and women have an equal combination of both slow twitch and fast twitch fibers. However, some people inherit a high percentage of slow twitch fibers that enhance their performance in endurance activities, such as long distance runners. Most world class marathon runners have a very high amount of slow twitch fibers. World class sprinters or football players, for example, have relatively more fast twitch muscle fibers. Although both fiber types respond positively to strength training exercises, the fast twitch types experience greater increases in muscle size and strength, and thus may obtain greater and/or faster results from a strength training program.

Age

Another factor over which we have little control is age. Studies show that people of all ages can increase their muscle size and strength as a result of a safe and effective strength training program. However, the rate of strength and muscle gain appears to be greater from age 10-20, the years of rapid growth and development. After reaching normal physical maturity, muscular improvements usually don't come as quickly.

Gender

Gender does not affect the quality of our muscle, but does influence the quantity. Although men's and women's muscle tissue are characteristically the same, men generally have more muscle tissue than women do because muscle size is increased by the presence of testosterone, the male sex hormone. The larger the muscles, the stronger the person; this is why most men are stronger than most women.

Limb and Muscle Length

Another strength factor that is naturally determined is limb length. Persons with short limbs tend to be able to lift more weight because of advantageous leverage factors (arms and legs). Similarly, differences in strength development may come about because of variation in muscle length. Some people have long muscles, and some people have short muscles. Persons with relatively long muscles have greater potential for developing size and strength than persons with relatively short muscles.

Point of Tendon Insertion

Muscle strength is also influenced by the point of tendon insertion. For example, let's say Jim and John both have the same arm and muscle length. However, Jim's biceps tendon attaches to his forearm farther from his elbow joint than John's does. This gives Jim a biomechanical advantage: he is able to lift more weight than John in biceps exercises such as the Biceps Curl.

Other Important Factors

All of these factors affect our ability to gain strength and muscle development through training. Keep in mind, however, that the most influential factor in achieving good results is using a very slow, controlled lifting movement and lifting to the point of muscle fatigue. In addition to using good lifting technique, it is absolutely imperative that you not only train with intensity on a well-balanced program, but also give your muscles enough resting time between training sessions. Overtraining is a common mistake people make; it happens not only when you don't allow your muscles enough rest, but also when you train with too many sets and exercises for each muscle group.

Another mistake people make is doing the same program over and over again even after they have reached a plateau. Any time you 1) stop gaining strength or muscle size or 2) get bored, it is crucial that you change the program, so that you can go through a whole new phase achieving new results. We inherit most of these factors affecting strength from our parents, and they have a big impact on our size, strength, and appearance. It is very important that you not become obsessed with trying to look like a world-class body builder—or any other body type that is not your own. We are not all meant to look the same. It is very important that you learn about and accept your own body's characteristics and type, so you can develop a reasonable program specific to realistic goals and personal interests.

Growth and Development

Growth and development are complex, interdependent processes, influenced by a variety of factors throughout one's life. Growth can be defined as an increase in size of certain parts of the body or an increase in size of the body as a whole. Growth changes are quantitative and can be measured in several ways; for example, in inches or in pounds.

Development, on the other hand, is the process of growth and differentiation. This can be seen as a progression in skill or increasing function complexity. Developmental changes are qualitative, measured by a variety of tests, including psychological tests.

Factors Influencing Growth and Development

Growth and development begin at conception. Physical growth ends at a certain point; development is a lifelong process. Several factors influence each individual's growth and development. These vary from person to person, in intensity, and at different times in life. Factors such as heredity, culture, nutrition, family, and the caretaking environment influence growth and development.

Other aspects, which have been seen affecting different stages of development in individuals, include geographical residence, climate (humidity and temperature, altitude, and season), socioeconomic placement, and the control of certain serious diseases of childhood.

Rates of Growth in Children

Growing children of the same age may develop at distinctly different rates, and even these large differences may be completely normal. Normal patterns should never be regarded as absolute standards or ideals. Even though the overall pattern of development may be similar from child to child, the rate of growth and development will be different for each. Every child is unique, and with this in mind, comparisons can be helpful. Simple but useful devices for comparing chronological ages at which a child reaches a particular developmental stage are called *age equivalents*. These are average ages at which children reach particular developmental stages.

Factors Affecting the Physical Growth and Development of Child

Child in the Mother's Womb

— Healthy mother gives birth to a healthy child. So it is very necessary that Physically, Environmentally and Mentally the mother is in sound health when the child is in the mothers womb.

— Any fever, rash, body aches etc. should be immediately reported to the doctor during first three months of Pregnancy.

— Mothers should avoid any sort of drugs, not prescribed by a Gynaecologist during the first 20 weeks of pregnancy.

— The Child in the mother's womb should also be safegaurded from radition during the first 20 Weeks. Recent studies have shown that excessive ultrasound sonography conducted during pregnancy may be harmful.

— Diseases like Toxoplasma, Rubella (German Measles), Cytomegalric virus, Herpes,Vericella,etc. can affect the child in the mother's womb.

The mother should be vaccinated with the available vaccines against tetanus. To protect against Rubella, MMR (Mums, Measles and Rubella) Vaccine can be administered.

Heriditory Diseases

Such cases can be referred for Genetic study. However there is no satisfactory Genetic study centre in Calcutta at present. Ultasonographic screening,chromosomel mapping. Gene therapy, enzymatic studies, metabolic studies are different techniques that are used at advanced medical centres mostly abroad to ascertain Genetic abnormalities in the foetal stage.

Nourishment of the child in the womb

Balanced healthy diet should be taken by the mother. No restrictions in diet in normal cases of Pregnancy. Progressive Gain in the weight of the mother is a positive sign. Mother should have normal Haemoglobin.

Neo natal Child

The first 28 days of the child after birth is a very delicate and critical period. The mother has to be very vigilant to appreciate if child is unwell or sick. The mother should take the child to a doctor if there is any rash, fever, vomitting, diarrohea, improper feeding, lethargy, abnormal movements of limbs etc.

Apart from the routine Vaccination- B.C.G, Polio, Tripple antigen. Today vaccination is available against a number of diseases.

— Vaccines are available against Measles, MMR (Measles, Mumps and Rubella), Hepatitis B, Haemophillic Influenza,(HIB) Meningitis Pneumonia and Rabbies.

— Vaccines against Chicken Pox and Hepatitis A are also on the verge of being available in India.

— Vaccination of your child against these diseases should be done at the right time.

Blood, blood vessels and exercise

A number of physiological changes occur in the body as we age, including a decrease in heart's ability to pump blood. New findings show that blood vessels in the legs adapt to reduced cardiac output by regulating the flow of blood to the leg muscles during exercise.

Physical Activity and Older People

The first International Consensus Statement on physical activity, fitness and health suggested that physical activity was an umbrella term that has multiple dimensions. Forms of physical activity such as exercise, sports and dance are considered as sub-categories of physical activity.

Physical Activity and Exercise

Physical activity has been defined as:

"any bodily movement produced by skeletal muscles that results in energy expenditure"

It is contrasted with exercise, which has been defined as:

"Leisure time physical activity (which is) planned, structured and repetitive bodily movement undertaken to improve or maintain one or more components of physical fitness"

Physical Activity and Active Living

While physical activity can be used as the general umbrella term described above, it is also used to describe a more specific form of activity more closely identified with active living. International and other consensus statements – for example from the US Surgeon General and the Department of Health – have identified the importance of participation in regular physical activity and active living in health promotion.

Physical activity and active living – a new health promotion message?

The concept of physical activity represents a recent change and a challenge to those involved in health promotion with older adults. It allows the possibility of integrating regular physical activity into everyday living, for example through the promotion of brisk walking, cycling, gardening and the use of stairs. It is an inclusive message and removes the need to plan activities such as a visit to the leisure centre, sports club or local fitness centre which often involve time and expense.

Sport and activity for all?

While evidence suggests that active living messages and activities such as walking and cycling are popular among older adults, it is important to promote a range of activities such as exercise classes in the gym or joining a fitness club and to provide opportunities to take up a new or continue with a sporting interest. While many older adults do not associate themselves with, or may be apprehensive about sporting and exercise opportunities, others, particularly those in their middle years, will have experienced a range of activity choices at school and during adulthood.

The expansion of sporting and exercise opportunities during the 1980s and 1990s through the promotion of Sport for All, and the increase in leisure centres and fitness and health clubs, suggest that many older adults will want the opportunity to continue these activities at a level of their own choosing.

Moreover, providers should beware of stereotyping older adults by directing them towards 'gentler' activities. With appropriate planning, adaptations and consideration of safety factors, opportunities provided for older adults should reflect a range of needs, capacities and interests.

Importance of Physical Activity in Old Age

There is growing evidence of the importance of physical activity for the older adult. The World Health Organization, the American College of Sports Medicine, and Young and Dinan, have identified the range of benefits of participation in regular physical activity for older adults. These include immediate and long-term physiological, psychological and social benefits particularly for certain conditions directly associated with old age.

> "A regular programme of moderate exercise is a very appropriate recommendation for almost all older adults. Moreover, there is no known pharmacological remedy that can so safely and effectively reduce a person's biological age and enhance his or her quality-adjusted life expectancy."

Physical activity and successful ageing

The adoption of a more physically active lifestyle can add years to life, even for previously inactive people. There is increasing evidence of the benefits of physical activity in relation to disease prevention, mobility, independence and quality of life. However, there is often a rather negative view and image of older adults expressed through the portrayal of age-related changes in functional capacity as a decline. Current policies consistently emphasise the need for strategies to promote successful ageing, which will enable older adults to maintain their capacity to undertake all the activities of daily living and to maintain their social networks. Specific types of physical activity can:

— significantly improve functional capacity and strength, which subsequently helps to maintain independent living and caring skills, and

— provide psychosocial benefits by improving mood and anxiety, leading to improved quality of life.

These benefits can be achieved both by healthy older adults and by the frail and very old. However, adaptations to the programming of exercise may be necessary for those with medical conditions and disability.

Striking a balance between disease prevention, the maintenance of independence, and improving quality of life is an aspiration expressed by older people themselves and provides a more optimistic view of successful ageing.

The benefits of physical activity

The benefits of physical activity include:

— Disease prevention and management, and improvements to quality of life

— Psychological benefits

— Social benefits

— Reduction in the complications of immobility

— Reduction in costs of health and other services.

Disease prevention and management, and improvements to quality of life

Physical activity can bring the following benefits:

— Reduced risk of coronary heart disease and stroke . It is estimated that 37% of coronary heart disease can be attributed to inactivity .

— All cause mortality has been shown to be significantly reduced by introducing exercise alone or exercise as part of a comprehensive rehabilitation programme for patients with coronary heart disease.

— Reduced impairment and improved strength in people with a variety of neurological disorders (e.g. neuromuscular disease or stroke).

— Improved walking ability and time for patients with intermittent claudication (leg pain).

— Reduction and control of high blood pressure through aerobic exercise and Tai Chi.

— Potentially favourable modifications to blood lipids.

— Reduced risk of developing type 2 (late onset) diabetes.

— Enhancements to the immune system.

— Prevention of post-menopausal osteoporosis, and protection against osteoporotic fractures by reducing the risk of falls.

— Weight control and management, although it is unclear whether weight loss in older people can be achieved through exercise.

— Potential improvements in disability, physical performance and pain in people with osteoarthritis of the knee.

— Increased functional capacity in patients with rheumatoid arthritis.

— Reduction in risk of, and treatment of, non-specific lower back pain.

— Improved quality of sleep.

— Possible reduction in the risk of colon cancer .

— A reduction in accidental falls.

— Improvements in cardiopulmonary fitness in people with asthma.

— Improvement and maintenance in the components of fitness related to mobility and independence (e.g. joint mobility, strength, power, endurance, gait, balance, co-ordination, motor skills and cognitive functioning).

— Improvements in stair climbing and walking ability.

Psychological benefits

There is also increasing research into the role of exercise and its potential benefits in the treatment of mental health and in improving mental well-being. Some of these benefits include:

— a reduction in stress and anxiety, and overall psychological well-being

— a reduction in depression, which might be as effective as antidepressants

— improvement in perception of health, cognitive function, self-esteem and self-worth

— a reduction in loneliness and isolation.

Social benefits

While research has concentrated on evaluating the effect of exercise on measurable physical and psychological outcomes, the social gains, although more difficult to quantify, are equally important and are, in some cases, of particular relevance to adherence to physical activity. The potential benefits include: -

— enhanced social integration and acceptable touching unconnected with dependence

— formation of new friendships

— widening of social networks

— role maintenance and new role acquisition

— enhanced inter-generational activity

— promotion of a more positive and active image of older people

— maintenance of caring skills.

Reduction in the complications of immobility

Immobility, particularly in frail older adults with multiple pathologies and disabilities, can lead to further complications, which can be reduced with specific exercise. These complications include:

— deep vein thrombosis (clotting)

— gravitational oedema (swelling of the legs caused by accumulation of fluid)

— contractures (thickening of the joint tissues leading to deformity)

— pressure sores

— faecal impaction (severe constipation).

Reduction in costs of health, social care and other services

Physical activity and exercise have been suggested as a cost-effective 'treatment' within the NHS. Physical activity has the potential to impact on the costs of:

— falls and accidental injuries – £1.7 billion per year

— coronary heart disease – £8.5 billion per year, including days lost due to death, illness and informal care

— poor mental health – £32 billion per year, including lost employment and benefits.

However, there is a danger that the emphasis on the potential for savings in health and social care costs leads to older adults being negatively portrayed as being a drain on services. This view may be reinforced by the demands made on service providers to make savings in this area.

Specificity of benefits

It must be remembered, however, that exercise and physical activity must be specific to its purpose. If the purpose of the exercise programme is to improve functional ability, then practice in functional tasks must be included in programming along with the normal components of fitness . If falls reduction is the purpose, then training in dynamic standing balance, and particularly Tai Chi, appears to be more effective than general seated exercise or walking. In dementia care the focus should be on mobility, endurance, stimulation and interaction.

Specificity must also be considered in terms of safety. Even vulnerable older patients can exercise safely, provided the exercise programme is appropriately designed and adapted to their needs.

How active are older people?

Activity levels among older people in the UK:

Despite the increase in the promotion of exercise and physical activity for prevention of functional decline and disease, people in the UK become less physically active as they age. Sedentary lifestyles are also very common among minority ethnic groups.

How many people are exercising enough to benefit health?

— In the 45-54 age group, only 39% of men and 35% of women participate in enough physical activity to benefit their health. Over the age of 74, only 14% of men and women regularly participate at this level.

— Just over 10% of men and women aged over 50 take part in sporting or exercise activities at least once a week. Nine per cent of men and 4% of women aged over 80 take part once a week. Exercises, cycling, social dancing and swimming are the most frequently mentioned activities, with exercises showing the least age-related decline.

— Twenty per cent of men and women aged over 50 walk a mile or more at least five times a week. By the age of 80 only 9% of women walk this often.

— In minority ethnic groups aged over 55, those participating in enough exercise to benefit health are approximately:
  — 20% of African-Caribbean men and 14% of women
  — 22% of Indian men and 2% of women
  — 15% of Pakistani men and 6% of women
  — 7% of Bangladeshi men and 1% of women
  — 13% of Chinese men and 14% of women.

How many older people are not exercising enough to benefit health?

— Among the over-50s, 40% of men and women are sedentary. Among the over-80s, 40% of men and 65% of women are sedentary.

— Only 3% of men and women aged over 50 take part in sporting or exercise activities at least five times a week.

— Nearly 90% of over 50s walk at a sufficient intensity or duration to benefit their health, less than once a week. Thirteen per cent of men and 15% of women aged over 70 are unable to walk for more than 5 minutes on their own.

— Twenty per cent of the over-50s climb no stairs at all in a week. Fifty per cent of the over-80s climb no stairs.

— In minority ethnic groups aged over 55, those who are sedentary account for:
  — 57% of African-Caribbean men and 59% of women
  — 67% of Indian men and 78% of women
  — 73% of Pakistani men and 85% of women
  — 85% of Bangladeshi men and 92% of women
  — 68% of Chinese men and 64% of women.

Physical activity among residents in care homes:

— The vast majority of residents in care homes are classed as inactive, with significantly more women (86%) than men (78%) in this category.

— Inactivity levels are highest in nursing homes, with about 90% of residents not having done a continuous walk of 15 minutes or more in the past month, and lowest in private residential homes (72% of men, and 82% of women).

— Overall, about four in five residents in care homes are inactive, compared to about two in five people aged 65 and over in private households. The difference between care homes and private households is largest in the youngest age cohort (65-74) and narrows gradually with advancing age.

— Almost half of all men (49%) and women (52%) in local authority residential homes either never or only very occasionally take trips outside the home.

Decline of functional capacity with age:

Even among healthy and active people, strength, endurance, bone density and flexibility are all 'lost' at a rate of about 10% per decade. Muscle power (the speed with which a muscle is used) is lost at an even faster rate of about 30% per decade. Inactivity significantly contributes to lower levels of functional capacity. The loss of physical function is exponential and will eventually cross a threshold level beyond which a person cannot maintain an independent life. For some older people, rising from a chair is difficult, and getting up off the floor without help is impossible.

The Allied Dunbar National Fitness Survey showed that, among those over the age of 50 in the UK:

— Twenty per cent of women and 14% of men do not have the flexibility to wash their hair comfortably.

— Nearly 10% of men and over 30% of women aged 50 – 74 do not have the aerobic capacity to walk comfortably at a 20-minute mile pace. Among 70-74 year olds, 35% of men and 80% of women are unable to maintain this pace of walking.

— Twenty five per cent of women and 7% of men aged 70-74 do not have enough strength in their legs to be confident of getting out of a low chair without using their arms.

— Forty-seven per cent of women aged 70-74 have insufficient leg muscle power to step up onto a bus without using their arms.

Together, the evidence of functional decline and decreased levels of physical activity associated with ageing emphasises the importance of promoting physical activity to older adults.

Physical activity recommendations for older people

Organisations including the World Health Organization, the Department of Health, the British Heart Foundation, the Centers for Disease Control, and the American College of Sports Medicine agree that older people should be encouraged and helped to develop and maintain the practice of regular physical activity throughout their lives. Physical activity is regular if activities are performed most days of the week, preferably daily.

There are no national guidelines in the UK for physical activity specific to older adults, but the following is a summary of current recommendations for the adult population.

> The recommendation for the adult population is to take part in physical activity of a moderate intensity for half an hour, on at least five days of the week.

Ideally, people should aim to take part in physical activity of a moderate intensity for half an hour, on five days of the week or more. This is the level that has been found to have significant benefits to health. However, evidence also suggests that for the maintenance of independence once or twice a week is satisfactory but should be considered a minimum.

To benefit health, physical activity should be at an intensity that raises the heart rate sufficiently to leave the individual breathing more heavily than usual and feeling warmer.

A combination of regular recreational activities such as brisk walking, swimming and gardening combined with specific exercises to improve strength and flexibility will be effective for most older people.

A 'bit at a time' approach:

While the recommendation is moderate activity for half an hour on five days of the week, it should be acknowledged that any activity is better than none at all, and people should be encouraged to start at a level of activity with which they are comfortable. This may be as little as five minutes of activity to begin with, with the aim of gradually increasing in duration and intensity. Two sessions of 15 minutes, or three sessions of 10 minutes of moderate activity achieves a similar benefit to one single session of 30 minutes in middle-aged men.

The greatest gains are achieved when a sedentary person is encouraged to become a little more active more often. Fartlek training (speed-play, where the pace and intensity of exercise can be varied)can be used to ensure that the individual can exercise for longer without undue fatigue and with greater safety and comfort.

It must be remembered that training effects will only occur if the body is presented with an 'overload' i.e. more than it is used to. It is important to emphasise that any physical activity, either supervised or undertaken independently, must tax the body in some way for physiological changes to occur. Psychological and social benefits may not require such 'overload'.

Endurance activities:

Cardiorespiratory (aerobic) endurance activities increase the heart rate and increase breathingfor extended periods of time. They improve the health of the heart, lungs and circulatory system, and have been shown to delay and prevent some diseases. Examples include brisk walking, cycling, swimming, heavy housework or gardening, dancing and jogging. Suggestions for intensity and frequency are 15-60 minutes of continuous aerobic exercise on at least three days of the week but preferably daily.

Muscular strength and power:

Muscle strength and power exercises can help older adults perform general activities of daily living (such as climbing stairs, rising from a chair with ease, lifting and moving household objects), and may also help to offset bone loss. Strength and endurance exercises for all major muscle groups should be done two to three times a week for 30-60 minutes (10-15 repetitions of 8-10 exercises at 30-40% of maximum strength. This could be a mix of supervised and unsupervised (home-based) activity. When working with vulnerable older patients, isotonic work (which involves the movement of a joint) is preferred even though there is no evidence that either moderate activities or isometric (where the joint is static) strength work (5-10 seconds) increases their risk of a clinical event.

Bone-building exercises:

To stimulate bone activity the American College of Sports Medicine recommends exercises that target the main fracture sites (three sets of 6-10 repetitions at 85% of the individual's maximum strength). This prescriptive approach may not be well tolerated and a more realistic number of repetitions and sets at a lower intensity may be necessary. Squeezing tennis balls daily for 10 minutes increases wrist bone density. Particular emphasis should be placed on strengthening the spine, hip and wrist. Sit-ups are no longer recommended for any age group but are particularly risky for those with low bone density as they increase the risk of spinal fractures. Instead, the erector spinae muscles should be targeted with prone (lying on your front) back extensions.

Balance exercises:

Balance exercises help prevent falls, and can be incorporated into strength training exercises. For example, lower body exercises for strength that require standing are also balance exercises. However, balance has both static and dynamic components and balance exercises should reflect this. Tai Chi and aqua-aerobics help improve balance, but changes in head and eye movement, sway training and gait (multi-directional walking) all tax balance. Balance exercises are ideally performed for between 10 minutes and one hour, at least three times a week.

Flexibility :

Stretching helps keeps the body supple and flexible and can help maintain freedom of movement and the ability to perform everyday tasks. Stretching of all major muscle groups through the fullest range of movement should be done regularly, before and after strengthening or aerobic exercise, and at least five times a week if not daily. Initially stretches should be held for 8-10 seconds to be effective.

World Health Organisation Recommendations:

"No group can benefit more than older persons from regularly performed exercise. Aerobic Exercise has long been an important recommendation for preventing and treating many of the chronic and typically age-associated diseases. Moreover, research indicates that strength training is necessary both to stop or reverse sarcopenia and to increase bone density. Increasing muscle strength and mass in older persons is a realistic strategy for maintaining this group's functional status and independence. The following recommendations for aerobic and strength-training exercises are appropriate for individuals aged 60 and older. Any exercise programme should of course first be discussed with one's health care provider."

Aerobic exercise:

Older persons should build up to at least 30 minutes of aerobic exercise – for example walking, swimming, water exercises and stationary cycling – on most, if not all, days.

Strength training:

The following regimen allows the individual to maintain bone and muscle strength. In order to continue to strengthen muscle and bone, one should steadily increase the intensity (weight) of the workout. Recommendations are:

- Strength training 2 to 3 days a week, with a day of rest between workouts.
- In a fitness centre, 1 set of 8 – 12 repetitions on 12 or more machines.
- At home, 2 to 3 sets of 8 to 12 repetitions using 6 – 8 different exercises.
- When repetitions can be made in good form with ease, weight lifted should be increased.

Impact of Exercise and Physical activity on the Gastrointestinal tract

The impact of exercise and physical activity on the gastrointestinal tract is an area of emerging interest. During the past two decades research was mainly directed towards the hazards of strenuous exercise, especially gastrointestinal symptoms. In recent years, however, interest has also focussed on the potential benefits of physical activity on the gastrointestinal tract. Several studies indicate an inverse relationship between physical activity and risk of gastrointestinal related diseases such as colon cancer, diverticular disease, cholelithiasis, or constipation. While the prevalence of these diseases is relatively high and increases with age, participation in physical activity is relatively low and decreases with age.

"Exercise" is considered as voluntary activation of skeletal muscle leading to short term effects (for minutes or hours) while "physical activity" is considered as repetitive exercise periods leading to long term effects (for days, weeks, months, or years). Nevertheless, in patients with gastrointestinal diseases physical activity may inhibit muscle loss, and improve appetite, functional capacity, and general well being by positive mood changes.

Hazards

Gastrointestinal symptoms such as nausea, heartburn, diarrhoea, and gastrointestinal bleeding are common during exercise, especially during vigorous sports such as long distance running and triathlons. In general, these symptoms are transient and can be considered protective for critical organ damage: its progressive nature causes the athlete to reduce exercise intensity or duration. Sometimes the symptoms may be so serious that they can limit exercise performance severely and even participation in physical activity.

Incidence rates during prolonged exercise vary mostly from 20% to 50%, depending on factors such as mode, duration, and intensity of exercise, type of symptom, age, training status, sex, dietary intake, occurrence of gastrointestinal symptoms at rest, and method of investigation. In particular, exercise intensity seems to be an important factor provoking gastrointestinal symptoms. The mechanisms by which exercise causes gastrointestinal symptoms are not well known. Decreased gastrointestinal blood flow, increased gastrointestinal motility, increased mechanical bouncing, and altered neuroendocrine modulation are postulated. All of these mechanisms are associated with exercise intensity. While most gastrointestinal symptoms do not hamper the athlete's health, gastrointestinal bleeding may be a serious problem.

Most often the type of bleeding is occult and transient, although anecdotal case reports document acute massive upper and lower gastrointestinal bleeding. Repeated gastrointestinal bleeding during training and competition may contribute to iron deficiency and anaemia. Also, endotoxaemia, malabsorption, gastrointestinal tract inflammation, and hypersensitivity reactions have been postulated to occur. All of these effects, however, can mostly be prevented by appropriate dietary (for example, sufficient fluid intake) and other precautions (for example, avoidance of large amounts of aspirin and non-steroidal anti-inflammatory drugs).

In addition to gastrointestinal symptoms, unfavourable effects of exercise on liver function and peptic ulcer disease have been reported. However, in well trained endurance-type sportsmen the increase in liver size can be interpreted as a physiological adaptation to increased energy expenditure rather than an expression of liver damage. Abnormal high serum levels of bilirubin, aspartate aminotransferase, and alkaline phosphatase are seldom observed in blood, underlining the fact that prolonged strenuous exercise does not lead to serious hepatic damage. Only under extreme exercise conditions, such as heat shock, may hepatic damage occur.

In the elderly, long term physical activity even may improve liver function. Epidemiological studies show that physically demanding occupations may enhance the risk of peptic ulcer disease, independent of several other risk factors such as social class. However, these studies were hampered by some limitations and pitfalls which question their conclusions. Recently, no relationship between a history of peptic ulcer and leisure time physical activity was found. Physical activity may even contribute to healing of gastric and duodenal ulcers by normalisation of the microcirculation at the ulcer regions.

The potential benefits of physical activity concern mainly effects on cancer risk, cholelithiasis, gastrointestinal haemorrhage, inflammatory bowel disease, diverticular disease, and constipation.

Gastrointestinal Cancers

To date, the risk of oesophageal, bile duct, or gall bladder cancers have not been examined in relation to physical activity. Concerning stomach cancer, the data are controversial: one study reported a reduced risk while two did not. No relationship between physical activity and risk of pancreatic cancers has been found, whereas rectal cancer risk was unrelated to physical activity in the majority of studies. In contrast, there is overwhelming evidence that physical activity reduces the risk of colon cancer. Despite different methods of assessing the amount and different types of physical activity (at work or during leisure time), there is consistent evidence that physically active men and women are at a reduced risk of colon cancer (up to 50% reduction in incidence).

This effect is independent of other risk factors such as diet and body weight characteristics. The types of activity that may be of benefit in preventing colon cancer are largely unknown. Studies analysing dose-response relationships suggest that more intense activity may confer greater protection against the risk of colon cancer than less intense activity. The primary postulated mechanism is that physical activity reduces intestinal transit time which would limit the time of contact between the colon mucosa and cancer promoting contents. Enhancing intestinal transit time may indirectly affect the risk of colon cancer by lowering secondary bile acid concentration or by increasing faecal short chain fatty acids. Other mechanisms related to colon cancer risk, such as impaired immune function, specific dietary intake (for example, large amounts of alcohol or fat, low amounts of dietary fibre), or an increase in body mass index, insulin resistance, prostaglandin and triglycerides levels, body iron stores, and/or free radical scavenging enzyme activity, can be altered favourably by physical activity.

Cholelithiasis

Several studies have been published on the relationship between physical activity and cholelithiasis. While early studies yielded controversial results, most of the later studies suggest a protective effect of physical activity. Many of the earlier studies in particular are hampered by several methodological drawbacks: no control for potential risk factors other than age (for example, body weight or diet), small sample sizes, limited methods for physical activity assessment, and low variability in physical activity among subjects. Furthermore, it cannot be ruled out that in some studies the level of physical activity was already reduced as a result of the onset of disease.

Two recent large prospective studies showed a relative risk (RR) of cholelithiasis of 0.63 in men and 0.69 in women when comparing the most active with the most inactive subjects, whereas sedentary lifestyle (watching television or sitting) resulted in an increased risk. A clear dose-response relationship was observed, independent of several potential risk factors, strongly suggesting that (symptomatic) cholelithiasis can be prevented by physical activity, even beyond its benefit for control of body weight or diet. The mechanisms by which physical activity may influence the pathogenesis of gall stones are poorly understood but decreased biliary cholesterol secretion, and enhanced gall bladder and colonic motility, all known to be important for gall stone formation at rest, are postulated.

Moreover, many factors which are related to an increased risk of cholesterol gall stone disease, such as glucose tolerance, high serum levels of insulin, triglycerides, and various gall bladder regulatory hormones such as cholecystokinin, and low serum levels of high density lipoprotein cholesterol, are favourably altered by physical activity.

Gastrointestinal Haemorrhage

The only study which examined gastrointestinal haemorrhage

and physical activity was a prospective cohort study with three years of follow up in 8205 elderly subjects. Only severe gastrointestinal haemorrhage was investigated. Physical activity was measured by self reported frequency of walking, gardening, or vigorous physical activity (resulting in sweating) three years before the study baseline. A summary variable for the three activities was also calculated. For those participants doing the activity at least three times per week, RR was significantly lower for walking (0.6) and for the summary variable (0.7) in comparison with sedentary subjects, independent of several other risk factors such as age, sex, mobility, body mass index, or health status. The RR for gardening (0.8) and vigorous physical activity (0.7) was not significantly lower. The authors hypothesised that a relatively increased gastrointestinal blood flow in physically active subjects reduced the risk of gastrointestinal haemorrhage.

Inflammatory Bowel Disease

A limited number of studies have investigated the preventive effect of physical activity on Crohn's disease (CD) or ulcerative colitis (UC). Sonnenberg was the first to show a beneficial effect of physical activity by comparing incidence rates of inflammatory bowel disease among several occupations in 12 014 individuals. Sedentary and physically less demanding occupations were associated with a higher risk of inflammatory bowel disease than physically demanding occupations.

Persson and colleagues confirmed this association in a case control study in patients with CD, but not with UC. They found RR values of 0.6 and 0.5 for weekly and daily exercise, respectively. Since then, inconsistent results have been obtained: one case control study showed a reduced risk, both for physically active CD and UC patients, while another study in CD patients did not. Postulated underlying mechanisms were the stress reducing effects of physical activity as well as changes in local neuro-immuno-endocrine effects.

While the preventive effect of physical activity remains inconclusive, it has become clear that physical activity is not harmful for patients with inflammatory bowel disease, despite acute exercise related responses, such as increased serum malondialdehyde levels and activated neutrophils. Nevertheless, physical activity should be promoted as these patients have muscle weakness and are at risk of osteoporosis. This risk is especially high with glucocorticoid medication, which causes muscle atrophy and weakness, osteoporosis, and osteopenia. In addition, physical activity may reduce disease activity and improve physical health, general well being, perceived stress, and quality of life.

Diverticular Disease

A possible role of physical activity in reducing the risk of diverticular disease was suggested by observations of Manousos and colleagues who found that diverticular disease was more prevalent among subjects with sedentary occupations than in more active occupations. Recently, Aldoori and colleagues also observed an inverse relationship with physical activity in a prospective cohort of 47 678 American men during four years of follow up. After adjustment for several factors such as dietary fibre intake, overall physical activity reduced the risk of symptomatic diverticular disease (for highest versus lowest extremes, RR=0.63). Risk reduction was stronger for vigorous activity (RR=0.60) than for non-vigorous activity (RR=0.93, NS). Several specific activities reduced the risk of diverticular disease but only for the combination of jogging and running was the inverse relationship statistically significant. An increase in colonic motor activity via hormonal, vascular, and mechanical aspects, leading to a reduction in colonic transit time, was postulated as an underlying mechanism.

Constipation

Several cross sectional studies have shown an inverse independent relationship between constipation and physical activity. Also, two case control studies showed that the defecation pattern of runners was "better" (less firm stools, higher defecation frequency, higher stool weight) than in inactive controls, a finding which could not be confirmed by the study of Klauser and colleagues. Inconsistent results were observed in patients who participated in a physical activity programme. Meshkinpour and colleagues studied eight constipated patients during four weeks of light physical activity (walking five days a week for one hour a day). The distance walked each day progressively increased from 2.9 to 5.2 km, but constipation did not change. Both Karam and Nies and Resende and colleagues showed an improvement in defecation pattern and reduced laxative use after a combined physical activity/nutrition programme in elderly patients but the effect of physical activity alone was not studied.

In all of these studies physical activity was of relatively low intensity. Thus the effect of physical activity on constipation seems likely, but has not been proved. Underlying mechanisms are unclear but a favourable effect on colonic motility, decreased blood flow to the gut, biomechanical bouncing of the gut during running, compression of the colon by abdominal musculature, and increased fibre intake as a result of increased energy expenditure have all been reported.

Biological Mechanisms

As mentioned above, the mechanisms by which exercise and physical activity influence the gastrointestinal tract are poorly understood although decreased gastrointestinal blood flow, increase in gastrointestinal motility, increased mechanical bouncing, and neuro-immuno-endocrine alterations are postulated. However, most of the described mechanisms have only been investigated after acute bouts of exercise. Whether or not these mechanisms are predictive of the long term effects of physical activity remains to be elucidated.

Gastrointestinal Blood Flow

During exercise, blood will primarily be shunted to the skin and exercising muscles at the expense of the gastrointestinal tract. Rowell and colleagues found a 60-70% decrease in splanchnic blood flow in humans exercising at 70% of maximal oxygen consumption (O2max). At maximal exercise intensity, splanchnic blood flow may be reduced by about 80%. Ischaemic damage has been proposed as a causal mechanism of gastrointestinal bleeding during and after exercise. Although gastrointestinal blood loss is transient, increased faecal antitrypsin and lysozyme concentrations after exercise have been found, indicative of local mucosal damage with an inflammatory response. Transient post-exercise lesions from the stomach to the colon have been observed in athletes and the histological picture indicates ischaemic damage.

Critical ischaemic levels may be reached under extreme exercise conditions when hyperthermia, hypohydration, hypoglycaemia, hypoxia, or a combination of these factors are present. In addition, changes in blood viscosity, erythrocyte deformability, and aggregability during exercise may further compromise local blood flow. Epithelial cells become deprived of metabolic substrates leading to necrosis and mucosal bleeding. In theory, critical ischaemic levels and accumulation of metabolic waste products may induce malabsorption, hypersecretion, and increased gastrointestinal permeability with endotoxaemia. Findings for the effect of exercise on absorption and acid secretion are inconsistent: both a decrease or no change in absorption and acid secretion have been reported. Exercise induced increases in intestinal permeability and mild leakage of endotoxins into the portal circulation have only been found at higher intensities.

Gastrointestinal Motility and Bile Salt Metabolism

Data on the effect of exercise and physical activity on gastrointestinal motility are scarce and mostly indirectly obtained and limited to acute exercise. The direct effect of exercise on gastrointestinal motility has been hypothesised to explain gastrointestinal symptoms such as heartburn (gastro-oesophageal reflux), vomiting, gastrointestinal cramps, urge to defecate, and diarrhoea. Gastric emptying of liquids and solids appears to be unchanged or slightly accelerated at lower exercise intensities. Above 70% O2max, gastric emptying is certainly delayed. The long term effects of gastric emptying are inconsistent: Carrio and colleagues found that basal gastric emptying was faster in runners than in controls while Rehrer *et al* found no difference.

Up to now two studies have focused on the effects of exercise and physical activity on gall bladder motility. An acute bout of aerobic exercise increased gall bladder ejection fraction slightly but insignificantly in a healthy non-obese female population. Also, the effect of physical activity was insignificant. In 27 obese female subjects who exercised (45 minute brisk walking five times per week) for 12 weeks, postprandial gall bladder ejection fraction increased significantly, but this increase, although larger, did not differ from that in the control group. Orocaecal transit time was reported to be unchanged, delayed, or accelerated after exercise. Harris and colleagues found that a high energy intake, which is probably correlated with intensive physical activity, was significantly correlated with fast orocaecal transit.

Studies of the effect of physical activity on colonic transit time have mostly been conducted in healthy subjects and their results are conflicting, probably due to methodological problems: four studies found accelerated transit time after physical activity while three observed no overall effect. Resende and colleagues observed no significant changes in gastrointestinal transit time in 12 immobile long stay patients after 12 weeks of individual sessions of massage and physical activity (five days a week, once a day). Research on the effect of exercise and physical activity on bile salt metabolism is mainly limited to animal studies. These studies showed that physical activity of moderate intensity increased bile acid excretion. Part of these changes were due to hyperphagia.

Research on the effect of physical activity and exercise on secondary bile acid formation and absorption in humans is scarce. In obese patients, a decrease in the secondary/

primary bile acid ratio has been observed after treatment with a subcaloric diet and graded physical activity. Sutherland and colleagues found that total faecal bile acid concentration was significantly lower in male distance runners than in sedentary men, while bile acid secretion was not different between groups. The lower faecal bile acid concentrations were mainly due to the higher fibre intake and subsequently higher stool weight in runners.

Mechanical Bouncing

The frequency of most gastrointestinal symptoms is almost twice as high during running than during other endurance sports such as cycling or swimming, where up and down movements are more limited. The mechanical vibration of the body is more than doubled in running compared with cycling. The way in which this bouncing of the gut affects gastrointestinal function is still unknown.

Neoro-Immuno-Endocrine Alterations

Many hormones associated with gastrointestinal function at rest (secretion, absorption, and motility) alter during exercise, in terms of plasma concentrations: cholecystokinin, vasoactive intestinal peptide, secretin, pancreatic polypeptide, somatostatin, peptide histidine isoleucine, peptide YY, gastrin, glucagon, motilin, catecholamines, endorphins, and prostaglandins. However, direct proof that these hormones alter gut function during exercise or induce exercise related gastrointestinal symptoms is lacking.

With respect to immune function, the current opinion is that physical activity of moderate intensity may protect against infections by inducing changes in the activity of macrophages, natural killer cells, lymphokine activated killers cells, neutrophils, and regulating cytokines. Severe exercise, however, can result in a transient reduction in natural killer cells and production of free radicals, which temporarily increases the risk of infection. Knowledge of optimal intensity and duration of physical activity for an optimal immunomodulating effect in athletes and in patients with gastrointestinal related diseases is lacking.

Role of Sports Physiotherapist

Sports physiotherapists help sportsmen and sportswomen operate at peak performance and give advice on prevention and recovery from injuries. They work in a team, with coaches, other health care professionals and sports scientists. Physiotherapists working in sport use a range of treatments, including manipulation, massage, taping, first aid, heat treatment, therapeutic exercise, electrotherapy, ultrasound, acupuncture and hydrotherapy. They need to keep accurate records of patient treatment and progress.

As well as working with top-level performers, many sports physiotherapists work with amateur sportsmen and sportswomen and people who take part in sport as a leisure activity. Sports physiotherapists may specialise in a particular sport, or alternatively in a particular aspect of physiotherapy, such as rehabilitation.

Hours and Environment

Most sports physiotherapists work irregular hours, including evenings and weekends. They have to be prepared to work up to 16-hour days when on tour with a team as they are usually working single-handed. They may have to attend training sessions and competitions or fixtures, which could include travelling in the UK or possibly abroad.

Treatment may be carried out in special treatment rooms or sports injury clinics, exercise areas, swimming or hydrotherapy pocls, sports centres or even at the side of the pitch at sporting venues.

Skills and Interests

To be a sports physiotherapist you should:

— have an interest and ability in health science and sport

— be concerned for the health and wellbeing of patients

— have excellent communication skills

— work well as part of a team with other health care professionals

— have good interpersonal skills

— be patient and sensitive, and show tact and tolerance when dealing with patients

— have good organisational and administrative skills.

Entry

Sports physiotherapists are chartered physiotherapists who have chosen to specialise in sport. To become a chartered physiotherapist you need a physiotherapy degree approved by the Health Professions Council. This will make you eligible for state registration and membership of the Chartered Society of Physiotherapy. Most sports physiotherapists have worked for several years as a chartered physiotherapist before specialising.

The minimum entry requirements for a degree in physiotherapy in England and Wales are three A level subjects at grade C or above, including a biological science, and four AS levels at grade B, including a biological science. You also need at least five GCSEs (A-C)/S grades (1-3), including maths, English and science subjects. In Scotland, you need five H grades at grades AABBB, with at least two science subjects. Details of all degree programmes are available from the Chartered Society of Physiotherapy.

It is advisable to obtain work experience in physiotherapy or attend an open day in a physiotherapy department, to help your application. Voluntary work as a physiotherapy assistant is an advantage.

It may be possible to start a physiotherapy degree course after doing a two-year Cadet Scheme, which covers a broad range of clinical experience. Ask your local hospital trust for details.

Individuals working as physiotherapy assistants can attend a part-time degree course. Football clubs may sponsor people on these courses.

Students with visual impairment can train on mainstream physiotherapy programmes with support from the Royal National Institute for the Blind (RNIB).

Training

Many sports physiotherapists will have taken a MSc in sport or rehabilitation science. A sports physiotherapist must hold a valid first aid certificate for sporting scenarios and be a member of the Association of Chartered Physiotherapists in Sports Medicine (ACPSM). This is a clinical interest group open to all chartered physiotherapists with an interest in sports medicine.

In England and Wales, funding is by a NHS means-tested bursary. Graduates with a good honours degree in a relevant discipline, such as a biological science, psychology or sports science, can study for an accelerated postgraduate Masters programme. NHS employees, at all levels, may be able to access learning and development opportunities through the NHSU, the new corporate university for the NHS.

Opportunities

Physiotherapists in sport may work in private practice, in health and fitness clubs and leisure centres. Some also work for sport associations or clubs. There is an increasing interest in sport in the UK, which is leading to more opportunities for working in sports physiotherapy. There are also opportunities to work abroad.

Adolescence: A "Risk Factor" for Physical Inactivity

Exercise is good for your health-a lesson learned from the ancients-but the recommendations for achieving such benefits has undergone a significant transition in the closing decades of the Twentieth Century. Most particularly, there has been a shift away from the importance of developing cardiovascular (aerobic) physical fitness and toward the promotion of life-long physical activity. This change has resulted from an understanding that the biological mechanisms linking exercise to health are not simply related to achieving high cardiovascular function but also in increasing caloric expenditure (obesity), weight-bearing activities (osteoporosis), and muscle strength (back problems, physical incapacity in the elderly).

In addition, it has been recognized that most diseases affected by exercise (such as coronary heart disease, hypertension, obesity, and osteoporosis) are a result of life-long processes, surfacing clinically in the older adult years. This observation has prompted an emphasis on promoting exercise habits in children and adolescents as the starting point of a life-style of regular exercise that will be maintained through to adulthood. That is, the introduction of exercise early in life with the key issue of persistence of activity has replaced an emphasis on improving physical fitness to threshold levels.

This shift in the exercise-promotion paradigm necessitates a parallel change in focus toward behavior modification rather than exercise training. But in developing this strategy many questions have arisen. How can young people best be "turned on" to being physically active? Can it be truly expected that improving activity habits of an eight-year old girl will cause her to be a more active adult? Given programmatic and financial constraints, should the promotional focus be on certain populations of children who are at particular risk for a sedentary lifestyle (the obese, the athletic "failures")? Or should physical activity promotion be expanded to the pediatric population at large?

One particularly critical aspect of activity promotion for lifetime health surrounds its timing. It might be assumed that there are certain periods of development when efforts to introduce physical activity habits are more likely to 1) be successful, 2) create an optimal salutary effect on health risk, and 3) be sustained into adulthood. In fact, when guidelines for physical activity for children have been created, special attention has been focused on age-specific recommendations. There has been a growing recognition that the adolescent years may, in fact, serve as such a pivotal, critical period for activity promotion and particular guidelines have been suggested for this age group. Epidemiologic evidence suggests that levels of activity demonstrate a particular decline during the teen years, especially in females.

Adolescence is a key period for changes in certain health risk factors such as the appearance of the initial lesions of coronary artery disease and peak development of bone mineral density. Standing at the immediate threshold of adulthood, the adolescent's physical activity habits-as well as health risk factors-are more likely to track into the older years. Opportunities for participation in organized sports decrease in the teen years, while factors discouraging physical activity, such as access to automobiles, become more available. Increases in body fat in the female at puberty may serve to discourage participation in physical activities. The biological drive for physical activity wanes during adolescence at the same time that increasing independence allows teenagers to manage their own lifestyles. They are thus less influenced by parents and more by their peers, and motivation for physical activity depends more on social rather than biological or family factors.

Table 1. Physical Activity Guidelines for Adolescents

All adolescents should be physically active daily, or nearly every day, as part of play, games, sports, work, transportation, recreation, physical education, or planned exercise, in the context of family, school, and community activities.

Adolescents should engage in three or more sessions per week of activities that last 20 minutes or more at a time and that require moderate to vigorous levels of exertion.

Special groups deserve particular exercise prescriptions. For example, obese adolescents may benefit from a program of increased regular energy expenditure through physical activity. Blood pressure may be reduced in adolescents with hypertension by vigorous activity, 3-4 times per week.

These unique features of adolescence provide both risk and opportunities for exercise-health promotion. The following sections will examine these influences which affect the present and future physical activity of adolescents. Recognizing and understanding these factors may prove essential in developing strategies for exercise promotion at this critical period in life.

Physical Activity in Adolescence

Efforts to improve exercise habits in the population confront the clearly-established trend for a progressive decline in individual physical activity throughout the life span. The daily caloric expenditure (relative to body size) of an 18-year old is approximately half that of when he/she was 6 years old. In reviewing research data, Sallis concluded that during the school-age years, daily physical activity decreases at a rate of about 2.7% per year in males and 7.4% per year in females. Levels of activity steadily decline during the adult years as well. The percentage of adults in the United States who are sedentary generally increases 2-3 fold between the ages of 20 and 65 years.

It appears that this basic trend for declining activity during life has a biological basis. Evidence supports the presence of an inherent control center within the central nervous system which governs levels of activity. With increasing age, centrally-dictated caloric expenditure through activity declines, paralleling that of basal metabolic rate. The decline in physical activity with age is therefore largely intrinsic, the result of a fall in central drive as well as other biological factors, such as a decreasing skeletal muscle mass in older years. There is no question, however, that the shape of the physical activity-age curve, i.e., the rate of decline in activity, is infiuenced by extrinsic, or modifiable, factors. And this is where interventional strategies can be effective in improving habits of physical activity.

Critical to this approach is the identification and manipulation of psychosocial and environmental determinants which affect the individual's motivation and participation in physical activity. Evidence exists to suggest that the rate of decline of physical activity is particularly accentuated during the teenage years. The Youth Risk Behavior Survey indicated that 81% of boys in grade 9 participated in vigorous activity during 3 or more days in the week before the survey. This proportion decreased steadily during the high school years to only 67% in grade 12. Between the ninth and twelfth grades the percentage involved in such vigorous activity in girls fell from 61% to 41%.

The survey also revealed a downward trend in enrollment in physical education during the course of high school. In the ninth grade, 81% of females and 81% of males were participating in physical education. By their senior year, however, these numbers had fallen to 39% and 45%, respectively.

Riddoch et al. reported that 11-13 year old Irish boys participated in an average of 33 minutes of activity daily while those 14-16 years were active only 7 minutes a day. In females, mean values were 20 and 12 minutes, respectively. In the Muscatine Study, Janz and Mahoney used accelerometers to examine the relationship of sexual maturation and daily activity levels during adolescence. Average daily movement, expressed as counts per minute, was 30% less in the postpubertal compared to midpubertal boys. In girls, counts were 19% less at postpuberty compared to midpuberty.

The longitudinal study of Verschuur and Kemper involved 233 Dutch male and female teenagers using heart rate monitoring to assess activity. At age 12-13 years the boys and girls spent 1.3 and 1.2 hours per day, respectively, exercising at an intensity equivalent to 50% VO2max. By age 17-18, time had decreased to 0.5 and 0.8 hours per day, respectively.

It is not difficult to suggest explanations for this inordinate decline in physical activity during adolescence. A combination of intrinsic and extrinsic factors are juxtaposed during the teen years which make the adolescent particularly vulnerable to developing a sedentary life style.

The Decline of Biological Drive and Rise in Psychosocial Influences

During early childhood, daily energy expenditure through physical activity appears to be largely biologically-driven. That is, the three year-old who zips about the house does not make a conscious decision to exercise or not. At this age, motivation for physical activity, access to exercise facilities, and support of family members are generally not critical to level of habitual physical activity. As the child grows, the biological drive for exercise energy expenditure declines and extrinsic factors affecting activity levels become more influential.

This reaches a particularly critical point at adolescence, when the diminished inherent drive for activity coincides with increasingly important psycho-social factors which influence involvement in physical activity. Unfortunately, these extrinsic factors often act negatively to diminish activity levels during the teen years.

The motivation for physical activity for the typical adolescent, no longer a biological issue, is shaped by factors that involve peer acceptance, physical capabilities, sexual attractiveness, and self-concept. For the talented high school athlete, sports play satisfies these issues. But for the nonathletic teenager, physical activity may be the antithesis of these goals, which are met by "hanging out", rebelling from adult forms, and adopting strange dress or hair styles. For many teenagers, vigorous physical activity is simply not "cool."

These social barriers to regular physical activity are compounded by the growing need for independence with rejection of adult-oriented health goals. The adolescent becomes old enough to drive, has more money and access to fast foods, and increases exposure to cigarette smoking and drugs. All these factors combine to make regular physical activity and other healthy lifestyles unattractive options for many adolescents.

Gender and Body Composition

Epidemiologic studies consistently indicate that males are involved in more total and vigorous daily physical activity compared to females, and this is true during adolescence as well. In addition, as noted above, some reports suggest that the decline in habitual physical activity during the teen years is more exaggerated in girls. These data imply that adolescence may be a particularly high risk period for developing sedentary habits in females.

Females face social pressures that have historically linked physical prowess and athleticism to maleness, and gender differences in activity have traditionally been accounted for by perceptions that femininity is not consistent with vigorous activity and sports play. While significant progress in dispelling this concept has occurred, detrimental ideas concerning gender-appropriateness in sports play and physical activity persist. Social issues continue to act as important impediments to involvement in exercise by girls. In adolescence these influences are compounded by the burgeoning sexuality at puberty and strong desire for attractiveness to the opposite sex. In males, sexual desirability is often linked to physical capabilities in sports participation and physical activity.

In females, on the other hand, attractiveness is focused on physical features, often perceived as incompatible with vigorous physical activity. Inevitable changes in body composition at the time of puberty may also work to the adolescent female's disfavor. Rising estrogen levels in the early teen years promote an increase in body fat in females, while the androgenic influences of puberty augment muscle mass in males. A typical 8-year old girl has 16% body fat, while at age 14 she will be 22% fat.

The value will rise to 24-30% by the time she is 35 years old. This increased fat serves as an inert load that must be transported during weight-bearing physical activity. That makes exercise more difficult, causing a tendency to avoid physical activity, which in turn results in increases in body fat and diminished physical fitness. The end result of this cycle is entrenched sedentary habits in the young female during the teen years which are difficult to reverse.

Limited Access to Sports Play

Participation in organized sports activities is a valuable means of maintaining high levels of physical activity in a social setting (Katzmarzyk & Malina, 1998). During the elementary and middle school years, widespread involvement by youngsters in community sports teams such as soccer, swimming, and baseball has, in fact, permitted large numbers of otherwise athletic-unskilled children to become physically active. Once high school is reached, however, such "everybody plays" programs disappear, supplanted by highly competitive programs which are designed for the few who are sufficiently skilled to "make the team". Opportunities for intramural participation in high schools is also unusual, as financial constraints channel available funds to interscholastic programs.

Adolescent Physical Activity and Health Risk Factors

An improved understanding of the natural course of certain chronic diseases of adulthood has indicated a particular significance for health interventions during adolescence. Many of these diseases are outcomes of pathological processes which begin during the teenage years. It follows logically, then, that interventions designed to prevent or reduce the risks of these diseases are best introduced during adolescence. In addition, given the proximity of adolescence to the adult period when such diseases appear clinically, behavioral changes such as improved physical activity in teenagers should have the best chance of tracking into the adult years.

Several examples highlight this strategy. Osteoporosis, or decreased bone density, increases susceptibility to skeletal fractures and is a major cause of disability and death in elderly individuals, particularly women. The peak gain in bone mineral density occurs at 13-14 years of age, and 90 percent of adult bone mineral content is established by the end of adolescence. As weight-bearing activity stimulates bone growth, regular exercise during the teen years should be expected to be important in decreasing the incidence and severity of adult steoporosis.

In adults, the risk of coronary artery disease, the major cause of death in the United States, is reduced by both regular physical activity and increased physical fitness. This may occur from an ameliorating effect on coronary risk factors, particularly elevating HDL-cholesterol, or by some unknown direct effect on the coronary vasculature. The atherosclerotic lesions which lead to coronary artery obstruction in adults appear initially in these vessels on autopsy specimens of adolescents. Physical activity habits which can reduce the risk of future myocardial infarction are therefore optimally introduced during the teen years.

Obesity in adults carries an increased risk of atherosclerotic vascular disease, hypertension, stroke, type 2 diabetes, and other significant diseases. Since obesity in children and adolescents rarely causes medical complications, the risk for the overweight youngster lies in the chance that his or her obesity will carry over into adulthood. As would seem intuitive, the risk of doing so increases with age during childhood, such that the obese adolescent has an 80% chance of becoming an overweight adult.

Tracking of Physical Activity

Physical activities initiated during adolescence will persist, or track, through the adult years. The extent that this is true has not yet been well clarified. Studies investigating this question are hampered by lack of an accurate means of measuring physical activity in large populations, an inability to easily assess intensity of regular exercise, and the effect of significant subject dropout on study findings.

Glenmark et al. described correlation coefficients of r=0.64 and 0.48 for women and men, respectively, between physical activity (by questionnaire) at age 16 and 27 years of age. In a similar study, Barnekow-Bergkvist et al. found that leisure time activity at age 16 years in males decreased the risk of being sedentary at age 34 years by one-half.

In reviewing both retrospective and longitudinal tracking studies, Telama et al. concluded that these reports "indicate that physical activity and sport participation in childhood and adolescence represent a significant prediction for physical activity in adulthood. However, the relationship is very low, and, in some cases insignificant." In their own study of young Finns, they found stronger correlations between physical activity in adolescence and 12 years later in adulthood (r=0.21 to 0.26) than from age 9 to age 21 (r=-.01 to 0.15). The effectiveness of increasing activity behavior in adolescence as an antecedent to improving adult activity has not yet been examined.

Tracking of physical inactivity may be more impressive. Raitakari et al. reported that the probability of an inactive 12 year old remaining sedentary at age 18 years was 51-63% for girls and 54-61% for boys.

Strategies for Promoting Activity in Adolescents

Given that physical activity needs to be promoted as a life-long continuum, it is apparent that different age groups require separate strategies for promoting regular habits of activity. In all groups, however, creating an enjoyment of physical activity in which individuals can be successful and receive peer and family support is key.

Strategies for health promotion are best formulated around recognized age-specific determinants of such activity. Research among adolescents has indicated a number of factors that have been associated with involvement in physical activity in this age group. In general these center around opportunities for play, support of friends, and competence in physical activities. It is apparent, too, that the varying influences of cultural group, socioeconomic status, race, geography, and season must be considered when formulating interventional programs .

It is possible that the factors which threaten to diminish physical activity habits during adolescence can be utilized instead as means of exercise promotion. For example, the educational message that the individual can and should accept responsibility for his or her own health (and exercise habits) is consistent with the adolescent's growing need for independence. Similarly, providing the adolescent with a choice of activities may prove more effective than physical education programs that dictate a curriculum.

For instance, using community programs, it might be possible to offer a choice of activities such as rock climbing, in-line skating, or kayaking that would prove more appealing to the adolescent than traditional physical education programs. Taking a cue from anti-smoking programs, efforts could be made to make physical activities more attractive to teens as opposed to an unpleasant life of sloth (i.e., "it's cool to sweat"). Such efforts seem particularly pertinent to females, and the message that vigorous activity is important for girls needs to be continued to be emphasized. This can be supported through the promotional efforts of female athlete role models.

If intramural sports cannot be made available within the school program, such activities should be developed by community recreation departments. The availability of school gymnasiums, exercise rooms, and pools in evening hours could be geared specifically to adolescent groups.

The input of adolescents in creating such programs may be critical to their success. As the "consumers" of preventive efforts, cues as to what "works" may best come from the teenagers themselves. Providing them independence in formulating physical activity programs may also provide a means of increasing participation.

3

Heredity and Environment

Health is the culmination of many interacting factors, including the genetic constitution. Humans are genetically quite diverse. Current estimates are that each human being has about one variable DNA base for every 300 bases out of a total of about 3 billion base pairs. Variations in DNA sequence constitute the molecular basis of genetic individuality. Given genetic individuality, an equal state of health and of physical and mental well-being is unlikely to be achieved for all individuals even under similar environmental and lifestyle conditions. Some will thrive better than others and will remain free from disabilities for a longer period of time.

Allowing for such individuality, it should thus come as no surprise that there is a minority of adults who remain relatively fit in spite of a sedentary lifestyle. Genetic differences do not operate in a vacuum. They constantly interact with existing cellular and tissue conditions to provide a biological response commensurate with environmental demands. Genes are constantly interacting with everything in the physical environment as well as with lifestyle characteristics of the individual that translate into signals capable of affecting the cells of the body. For instance, overfeeding, a high fat diet, smoking, and regular endurance exercise are all powerful stimuli that may elicit strong biological responses.

However, because of inherited differences at specific genes, the amplitude of adaptive responses varies from one individual to another. Inheritance is one of the important reasons why we are not equally prone to become diabetic or hypertensive or to die from a heart attack. It is also one major explanation for individual difference in the response to dietary intervention or regular physical activity.

There is no universally agreed upon definition of fitness and of its components. Health-related fitness refers to the state of physical and physiological characteristics that define the risk levels for the premature development of diseases or morbid conditions presenting a relationship with a sedentary mode of life. Important determinants of health-related fitness include such factors as body mass for height, body composition, subcutaneous fat distribution, abdominal visceral fat, bone density, strength and endurance of the abdominal and dorso-lumbar musculature, heart and lung functions, blood pressure, maximal aerobic power and tolerance to submaximal exercise glucose and insulin metabolism, blood lipid and lipoprotein profile, and the ratio of lipid to carbohydrate oxidized in a variety of situations. A favorable profile for these various factors presents a clear advantage in terms of health outcomes as assessed by morbidity and mortality statistics. The components of health-related fitness are numerous and are determined by several variables, including the individual's pattern and level of habitual activity, diet and heredity.

Genetic Perspective

In general, genetic issues can be considered from two different perspectives. The first is from the genetic epidemiology perspective. Here the evidence is derived from samples of human subjects, particularly families, large pedigrees, relatives by adoption or twins. The data can be epidemiological in nature or be enriched by molecular studies. The second perspective is frankly molecular and pertains to transcription, translation, and regulatory mechanisms and how the genes adapt or come into play in response to various forms of acute exercise and of training. In this case, the tissue (generally heart muscle or skeletal muscle) is perturbed by an acute or a chronic stress and the changes are monitored. The emphasis is therefore on the molecular mechanisms involved int he adaptation. Both approaches are very useful in delineating how important genes are for a give phenotype.

However, they differ considerably in the type of information they can provide. The first approach is asking whether individual differences for a given phenotype are caused by DNA sequence variation, gene-environment interactions and gene-gene interactions seen among human beings and, ultimately, what are the genes involved and the specific DNA variants accounting for human heterogeneity. The second approach relies heavily on animal models with a focus on the role of various DNA sequences on regulatory mechanisms with no particular interest for the differences that may exist among members of the species. Although the literature presents evidence for a role of genetic factors in most of the health- related fitness phenotypes, the quality of the evidence varies according to the phenotype considered. Four major components of health-related fitness will be considered here.

1.*Morphological component*: Obesity (body fat content) and regional fat distribution are the phenotypes or morphological fitness that have been studied most by geneticists. Table 1 summarizes the trends emerging from several reviews regarding the contribution of genetic factors to obesity, regional subcutaneous fat distribution, abdominal visceral fat and bone density. The body mass index (BMI), subcutaneous fat (sum of skinfold thicknesses) and percent body fat derived from underwater weighing are among the most commonly used phenotypes in genetic studies of obesity. They are characterized by heritability levels reaching about 25% and at times higher.

Results from a few studies suggest that BMI and percent body fat may be influenced by variation at a single or a few genes, although there are conflicting results. The phenotypes associated with regional fat distribution are generally characterized by slightly higher heritability levels with values reaching about 30% to 50% of the phenotypic variance. The trunk to extremity skinfolds ration as a marker of regional subcutaneous fat distribution has been found to be influenced by major effects, possibly associated with variation at a single gene, suggesting that the pattern of fat deposition between the trunk and the limbs is significantly conditioned by genetic factors.

Table 1. An overview of trends in heritability date for selected factors of morphological fitness

Phenotype	Heritability[a]	Familial environment[b]
Body fat content	25%	Weak
Distribution of subcutaneous fat	30-50%	Weak
Visceral fat	30-60%	Unknown
Bone density	30-60%	Weak

a. Approximate proportion of the variation in the phenotype compatible with a genetic transmission after removing the effects of age and sex.
b. Conditions shared by individuals living together.

2.*Muscular component*: This fitness component is probably the one for which the evidence for a contribution of genetic factors is the least abundant. Two studies used family data to study familial transmission of muscular fitness. In one study, muscular endurance and muscular strength measurements were obtained in 13,804 subjects who participated in the 1981 Canada Fitness Survey. The results showed that about 40% of the phenotypic variance in muscular endurance and muscular strength could be accounted for by factors transmitted from parents to offspring. In the Quebec Family Study, the genetic effect of 21% for muscular endurance and 30% for muscular strength. These results suggest that the heritability of muscular fitness is significant and ranges from low to moderate.

Cardiorespiratory component

Cardiorespiratory fitness is a major component of health-related fitness and depends on a large number of phenotypes associated primarily with cardiac, vascular and respiratory functions. Measurements of submaximal exercise capacity and maximal aerobic power are generally performed to assess cardiorespiratory fitness. The contribution of genetic factors to these two phenotypes has been recently reviewed and estimates of heritability were found to be lower for submaximal exercise capacity (about 10%) than for maximal aerobic power (about 25%). These inherited differences in cardiorespiratory fitness may be partly explained by interindividual differences in heart structures and functions, but relatively little is known about the role of heredity on these determinants despite evidence for significant familial aggregation.

Because of the high prevalence of hypertension in most developed countries and its association with an increased risk of death from myocardial infarction of stroke, the genetic and non-genetic determinants of blood pressure have been extensively studied in various populations. Overall, it is clearly established that blood pressure aggregates in families and heritability estimates reported from various populations are remarkably similar, accounting for about 30% of the interindividual differences. More recently, several specific genes have been implicated in the determination of the susceptibility to hypertension.

3.*Metabolic component*: There is increasing evidence that the metabolic component of health-reiated fitness should be considered as an important element of the relationship between physical activity and health. The metabolic component refers to normal blood and tissue carbohydrate and lipid metabolisms and adequate hormonal actions, particularly insulin. A large number of studies have been reported on the genetics of blood lipids and lipoproteins, because of their predominant role in the etiology of cardiovascular disease. Briefly, genetic factors contribute to interindividual difference in blood lipids and lipoproteins with heritability estimates generally accounting for about 25% to as much as 98% of the phenotypic variance, depending on the trait considered with an average value of 50%. Major gene effects have been reported for most of the phenotypes including total cholesterol, LDL-cholesterol, HDL-cholesterol, various apolipoprotein concentrations and Lpa.

Highly significant genetic effects have also been reported for fasting glucose and insulin values as well as for plasma fibrinogen, a protein involved in blood clotting. The glucose and be characterized by lower heritability estimates (<25%) than for fasting values. The contribution of heredity to the various health-related fitness components thus ranges from low to moderate and, except for some phenotypes pertaining to muscular fitness and metabolic fitness, it rarely exceeds 50% of the phenotypic variance and is often below 25%. These low to moderate heritabilities should not be interpreted as an indication that genes are not important in the determination of these phenotypes. These highly complex phenotypes are undoubtedly influenced by a variety of interactions. There is increasing evidence to the effect that interactions between genes and environmental factors or between various genes are common and contribute to interindividual differences in health-related fitness phenotypes and, consequently, cannot be any longer ignored in the field of physical activity, fitness and health.

Heridity and Response to Exercise

Research has amply demonstrated that aerobic performance, stroke volume, skeletal muscle oxidative capacity and lipid oxidation rates are phenotypes that can adapt to training. For instance, the VO2max of sedentary persons increases, on the average, by about 20 to 25 percent after a few months of training. The skeletal muscle oxidative potential can easily increase by 50 percent with training and, at times, it may even double. However, if one is to consider a role for the genotype in such responses to training, there must be evidence of individual differences in trainability. There is now considerable support for this concept. Following exposure to training programs lasting from 15 to 20 weeks in 47 young men, some exhibited almost no change in VO2max, while others gained as much as on liter of O2 uptake. Such differences in trainability could not be accounted for by age (all subjects were young adults, 17 to 29 years of age) or gender (all young men). The initial (pre-training) level accounted for about 25 percent of the variance in the response of VO2max; the lower the initial level the greater the increase with training. Thus about 75% of the heterogeneity in response to regular exercise was not explained.

Similar individual differences were observed for other relevant phenotypes such as indicators of endurance, markers of skeletal muscle oxidative metabolism, markers of adipose tissue metabolism, relative ratio of lipid and carbohydrate oxidized, fasting glucose and insulin levels as well as in their response to a glucose challenge, and fasting plasma lipids and lipoproteins. All these phenotypes respond to regular exercise in the young adults of both sexes. However, there are considerable individual differences in the response of these biological markers to exercise-training, some exhibiting a high responder pattern, while others are almost non-responders and with a whole range of response phenotypes between these two extremes.

What is the main cause of the individuality in the response to training? Bouchard says, they believe that it has to do with as yet unidentified genetic characteristics. To test this hypothesis,they have no performed several different training studies with pairs of identical (MZ) twins, the rationale being that the response pattern can be observed for being that the response pattern can be observed for individuals having the same genotype (within pairs) and for subjects with differing genetic characteristics (between pairs). They concluded from these studies that the individuality in trainability of cardiovascular fitness phenotypes and in response to exercise- training of cardiovascular risk factors is highly familial and most likely genetically determined.

The date are expressed in terms of the ratio of the variance between genotypes to that within genotypes in the response to standardized training conditions. Over a period of several years, 26 pairs of MZ twins were trained in their laboratory with standardized endurance and high intensity cycle exercise programs for periods of 15 or 20 weeks. After 10 weeks of training, the twins were exercising 5 times per week, 45 min. Per session at the same relative intensity in each program. These training programs caused significant increases in VO2max and other indicators of aerobic performance. They were also associated with a decrease in the intensity of the cardiovascular and metabolic responses at a given submaximal power output.

For instance, when exercising in relative steady state at 50 watts, there were decreases in heart rate, oxygen uptake, pulmonary ventilation, ventilatory equivalent of oxygen and with an increase in the oxygen pulse. These various metabolic improvements were, however, all characterized by a significant within-pair resemblance. They have made the same observation for the alterations seen in skeletal muscle metabolism following training studies performed on skeletal muscle biopsies obtained before and after the training program in a good number of MZ twin pairs. Nonpharmacological interventions designed to improve the cardiovascular risk profile center around the cessation of smoking, weight loss by means of dietary restriction and at times regular physical activity, dietary modifications aimed at fat, sodium and fiber intake, and regular exercise in order to improve health-related fitness. Among the expected changes associated with a regular exercise regimen, one finds in a group of sedentary and unfit adults a decrease in resting heart rate and blood pressure, a reduction in fasting plasma insulin level and its response to a glucose load, a decrease in plasma triglycerides and, occasionally, in LDL-cholesterol and total cholesterol, and an increase in plasma HDL-cholesterol.

Little is known about the individual differences in the response of these important clinical markers to regular exercise and about the role of genetic variation. They have used the MZ twin design to explore these issues in two studies. In one experiment, 6 pairs of young adult male MZ twins exercised on the cycle ergometer 2 hours per day for 22 consecutive days. The mean intensity of training reached 58 percent of VO2max and the program was designed to induce an energy deficit of about 1,000 kcal per day. Baseline energy intake was assessed and prescribed for the 22 days of the training program.

The diet prescription was fully enforced for each subject in the metabolic ward where they lived for the duration of the experiment. The second study was performed on 7 pairs of MZ twins who followed the same regimen for 100 days. The results of both studies are quite concordant. The program induced a significant increase in VO2max and a significant decrease in body fat content. Significant changes were observed in fasting plasma insulin and in the insulin response to an oral glucose tolerance test.

Plasma triglycerides, total cholesterol, LDL-cholesterol and apo B as well as the HDL-cholesterol to total cholesterol ratio were also modified. However, again, significant within MZ pair resemblance was observed for the response of fasting plasma insulin, and LDL-cholesterol ration were also modified. However, again, significant within MZ pair resemblance was observed for the response of fasting plasma insulin, and LDL-cholesterol, HDL-cholesterol, the HDL-cholesterol to total cholesterol ration and for the improvement in body fat content and in fat topography. Thus being genetically different translates into heterogeneity in the adaptation to exercise programs.

When Nick's friends asked him to take part in a casual Saturday afternoon game of soccer, he didn't realize that kicking a ball around on a muddy field would change his life. But as he chased after that damned ball, while his leg muscles cried out in pain and his lungs heaved like circus tents in a storm, Nick realized that his body had gone all to hell - after just a few short years of scoffing up thick slices of Yorkshire pudding and slugging down pints of ale each night after work. In the locker room after the game, Nick peered at his paunch, glared at his lardy shoulders, stole quick glances at his varicosed legs, and decided that maybe it was time to.... well....

do something. He wasn't sure exactly WHAT to do, and he wondered whether his preoccupation with his flabby belly was little more than bathos in the bathhouse, but gradually he developed a firm resolve to 'shape up'. By the next evening, he had purchased a nifty set of running shoes.

And Nick was not the kind of fellow to do things by halves. Just as he had eaten, imbibed, and lazed around really earnestly over the years, he began his new, fitter life by training with the steadfastness of a monk. Flab fell from his abdomen, muscles burst from his buttocks, sinews sprouted from his thighs, and his lungs expanded and deflated in a more relaxed manner as he cruised through his daily runs. Nick even began to enter races, and his 10-K times improved steadily. His first competition took 47 minutes, but soon he was at 46 minutes, then 45, made a big breakthrough to 42, and - after a year of hard training - broke the magical 40-minute barrier with a euphoric 39:55. Soon he was running in the 39s regularly, and he even surged through a sizzling 38:30 one beautiful autumn day.

But then, sadly, the improvements in performance stopped. Nick waited, and trained, and raced, and waited some more, but when not a single additional second dropped from his race times, he began to fiddle with his training, added more speed work, carried out hill repetitions, took up weight training, bought books about Olympic athletes, and even went to Kenya on holiday in hopes of adding some East-African speed to his legs. The result? He continued to run his races in his usual 38s and 39s. Nick began to face the hard truth - that he just wasn't going to improve any further. Now, Nick had entertained thoughts of running 10 kilometres in 35 minutes, and - if the truth be told - he had even had a secret longing which grew stronger each time he set a new PB. His hope was that he might be one of the lucky ones - someone to watch out for at races, someone who could be an elite athlete and actually win prize money from the sport.

Since all of those hopes were now dashed, Nick did the only thing he could do. He began to blame his mum and dad.

Poor old mum, hobbling down the street to the market, and dad, puffing on his blasted pipe and reading the paper at the fireside, why hadn't they given him more of the right stuff? Why hadn't mum done more training as a schoolgirl, taken up marathon running as a young woman, set age-group records after menopause, and encouraged Nick to be more active? Why hadn't dad chucked away his god-awful pipe? Surely that foul device had clogged Nick' s lungs with smoke as a child, thwarting his aerobic development.

Nick continued to resent his parents' poor influences for some time, but then one day at a race in London, Nick - for no apparent reason at all - decided to line up with the elite runners at the starting line. If he couldn't run a great 10K, he wanted to at least feel what it was like to rub shoulders with the great runners. As he stared at the slim bodies and determined faces next to him, he had a sudden realization: all of the parental training and coaching in the world would not have helped him. He was stuck in bad stock: his parents had simply not given him the genes of a Gebrselassie or a Kiptanui.

In fact, Nick' s soul - the soul of a running fanatic - was trapped in the body of a greengrocer. Nick returned to the middle of the pack of runners with a horrible realization: great athletes are born - not made. But was he right? Is it true that the most important thing an aspiring athlete can do is to choose the right parents, as the great Swedish exercise physiologist Per-Olof Astrand once claimed? Actually, no. Although athletic performance is influenced by genetics, scientific investigations have frequently found that it's even more dramatically shaped by training and motivation, not genes.

Identical Twins

Not surprisingly, many of these studies have focussed on what happens when twins embark on an exercise programme. The reason for using twins in the performance research is simple: if both twins and people plucked at random from the street begin a serious exercise programme, there will be a huge variation in response. Some individuals will improve their aerobic capacities by 50-60 per cent or more, others will achieve a more-usual gain of 20-30 per cent, and a few unfortunates will get an aerobic uptick of less than per cent. However, if genes are important, identical twins should respond in a very similar fashion.

If one member of a set of twins boosts maximal aerobic capacity (V02max) by 35 per cent, for example, the other should also raise aerobic power by about 35 per cent. If one twin lifts V02max by 10 per cent, his identical twin should also get about a I O-per cent gain. If performance is highly 'heritable,' eg, it can be passed on readily in genetic material, we would expect that identical twins would almost always respond to training in the same way. On the other hand, if identical twins develop quite different performance capacities, it would be hard to argue that genes play a major role in determining the response to training. For example, if one twin gains 50 per cent and his identical twin increases aerobic capacity by only 10 per cent, we can figure that something other than genes is determining their performances. After all, their genes are identical, but their responses to training are quite different.

Scientists interested in the genetics of performance are no slouches, so they usually include both 'monozygotic' and 'dizygotic' twins in their studies, as well as brothers and sisters. Somewhat surprisingly, it' s not hard to find twins for these studies. Although many people think that twinning is a fairly rare event, the truth is that about one out of every 100 births involves twins, which means that one person in 50 has a twin. About 33 per cent of all twin pairs are identical (monozygotic), which means that they originated from exactly the same sperm-egg combination and have precisely the same genotype (their genetic constitutions are identical).

On the other hand dizygotic (fraternal) twins, although born at the same time, come from different sperm-egg combos and are no more closely related genetically than 'normal' siblings. Dizygotic twins, brothers, and sisters share about 50 per cent of the same genes. As a result, if genes really do determine performance, we wouldn't expect dizygotic twins and siblings to respond to training as identically as identical twins. However, fraternal twins and sibs should be more similar than people chosen at random from the overall population.

To put it another way, monozygotic twins should have almost the same 10-K times, as long as their training is similar, dizygotic twins and siblings might have 10-K times a few minutes apart, and people chosen at random might have times ranging from 26:44 (the current world record) all the way up to 55-60 minutes. The less close the genetic relationship, the wider the variation. Bear in mind, though, that we can't determine how much of any single person's performance is determined by genes, but we can assess how much of the VARIATION in performance within a group of people is attributable to genes.

In other words, we can't tell Nick that, say, 40 per cent of his 10-K improvement from 47 to 38 minutes was the result of the DNA piloting his cells while the other 60 per cent resulted from his training, but we can estimate that 40 per cent of the variation in performance times in a population is due to genetic differences between members of the population. That's not very precise or individualised, but it does give us an indication of how important genes are in deciding what happens when people get serious about training. If 80 per cent of the variation was due to genetic factors, for example, we could sensibly conclude that the effects of genes far outweigh the effects of actual training.

So what have scientific studies actually found? Much of the best work has been carried out by Claude Bouchard, Ph.D., and his colleagues at Laval University in Quebec, Canada. In the early 1980s, Bouchard and co-workers decided to find out just how much variation in fitness could be present in a group of people who were training in a fairly similar manner. The goal was to eventually determine what portion of this variation was due to genetic factors and what portion was due to non-genetic influences such as nutrition, smoking habits, past exercise habits, age, socioeconomic status, etc. In one of the first studies, 24 similar, initially sedentary subjects trained in exactly the same manner for 20 weeks. Although the training was identical, the people responded to training in disparate ways.

Although the average gain in VO2max was 33 per cent, one individual had gained 88 per cent, while another had increased aerobic capacity by only 5 per, cent - with exactly the same training programme! Variation in actual performance, which was measured as the average power output a subject could sustain on a bicycle for 90 minutes, was also sizeable. Overall, performance soared by an average of 51 per cent after 20 weeks, and the biggest gainer was an individual who improved performance by 97 per cent, while the smallest improvement was made by a sad sack who advanced by just 16 per cent (less than 1 per cent per week). These and later findings taught the Laval scientists that there are 'responders' and 'non-responders' within any population of people.

The 'responders' make big improvements in aerobic power and performance as a result of their training, while the non-responders barely emerge from their sedentary physiological states, even after 20 weeks of vigorous work. Exercise scientists reckon that about 5 per cent of people in the population at large are high responders (they can improve by over 60 per cent), while about the same per centage are low responders (they improve by less than 5 per cent). The Laval researchers also found that the time scale of training responsiveness varies a lot between people.

Some are much better after just four to six weeks of training but may not improve after that, while others - the 'late bloomers' - are stagnant for six to 10 weeks and then really take off, improving their aerobic capacities by 20-25 per cent after 10 additional weeks of training. How significant are genes in determining responsiveness and in deciding if you're a responder, a non-responder, a quick responder, or a late bloomer? To check that out, the Laval investigators placed 10 pairs of monozygotic (identical) twins on a 20-week training programme. The 20 subjects trained four to five times a week, 40-45 minutes per session, with average training intensity set at about 80 per cent of maximal heart rate. After 20 weeks, aerobic power burgeoned by 14 per cent, and 'ventilatory threshold' ;L - the exercise intensity at which breathing rate begins to increase fairly dramatically - improved by 17 per cent.

The most important finding, however, was that identical twins did in fact respond almost identically to the training programme. For example, one twin upgraded V02max by 10 per cent, while his identical twin improved by 11 per cent. Another gained 16 per cent while his twin settled for 14 per cent. Yet a third pair rested at 25 and 22 per cent. Overall, most of the variation in VO2max was between, not within, sets of twins. However, this does NOT mean that genetics are the most important factor which determines performance. All the twin studies demonstrate is that genes are important; they do influence the way people respond to training. They don' t tell us that genes are more important than training and other factors.

We only know that genes do play some role and that identical twins will be more alike than dizygotic twins and siblings, who in turn will be more alike than non- ' related people. That's hardly earth-shaking news. And, in fact the twin research offers some 'twists' which suggest that genes play a 'supporting' - but not 'lead' - role on the performance stage. For example, 82 per cent of the variation in VO2max in the Laval twin study was due to genetic differences, but only 33 per cent of the difference in ventilatory threshold was attributable to genes. Somehow, genes were playing a strong role in setting aerobic capacity, but the environment (lifestyle factors and past differences in training) was considerably more important in fixing ventilatory threshold. That' s a key finding, since ventilatory threshold - and a closely related variable called lactate threshold - are often found to be the best predictors of actual endurance performance, better than aerobic capacity, anaerobic power, or efficiency of movement.

Married couples are equally similar

And there are other findings which put a dent in the idea that genes are paramount in shaping performance capability. For example, the Laval researchers found that spouses were as similar in their response to training as were brothers and sisters, even though the spouses were totally unrelated genetically. In other words, if Joe and Jean are married and begin training with Joe's brother John, Joe's gain in V02max is just as likely to be the same as Jean'.s as it is the same as John's! That' s hardly a ringing endorsement of the idea that genes play the crucial role in determining performance. In general, studies carried out with brothers and sisters suggest that genes explain only 20 per cent of the variation in observed performances.

Training and lifestyle account for the other 80 per cent - or four times as much! In addition, investigations which put mothers and their children on a training schedule have found that genetics explain just 28 per cent of the variation in V02max, even though a mum and her offspring share about 50 per cent of the same genes. That means that 72 per cent of the variation is due to training and other factors. Sorry, dads, but the news is even worse for you. Investigations of fathers and their children have been unable to suggest that genetics plays any role at all in explaining variation in aerobic capacity, even though dad and son/daughter are 50-per cent alike! In other words, a father and his son are no more likely to respond to training in a similar manner than are two people selected at random on the street.

Again, these findings hardly support the idea that great athletes are born, not made. But let's digress for a moment and consider why your mum is more important than your dad in determining how you'll turn out as an endurance athlete. The answer to this question rests inside tiny structures inside muscle cells called mitochondria, which provide most of the energy required for your endurance performances. The little mitochondria have their own genes, and all of the mitochondria in your body come from your mother, not from your dad, because your mum's egg contained mitochondria, while your father's penetrating sperm was mitochondria-free. As your foetal cells divided and formed muscle, nerve, and bone cells, they took with them mum's mitochondria.

If she gave you good little mitochondria, you have a decent chance of becoming an endurance athlete; dad's mitochondria just don't count. As you've guessed by now, genetics don't play the dominant role in producing top-level performances, but in addition to mother's mitochondria, there are some anatomical and physiological attributes which are highly heritable - and which can help you get to the finish line of a race more quickly. For example, your heart's 'coronary network' (the distribution and size of blood vessels within your heart) is genetically determined, as is the branching pattern of blood vessels which lead into your lungs.

Total heart size is mildly heritable, and the volume of the heart's left ventricle - the key internal chamber which sends blood to your muscles - may be strongly determined by genes. Muscle proteins, including key energy-producing enzymes, are also dictated by genes, as is muscle-fibre composition. If your mother and father had a high percentage of Type I muscle cells (the kind which have excellent aerobic potentials and promote superior endurance), your legs will probably also be biassed toward Type I cells, and you'll probably be a pretty decent marathoner.

In fact, some studies have shown that muscle composition - or more specifically, the percentage of Type I fibres - can explain up to 90 per cent of the variation in race times observed during the 26.2-mile race. Metabolism of fat is also at least partially genetically determined. However, the bottom line is that your genetic endowment is really just the stage upon which your training, nutrition, and motivation act out their important roles and produce your ultimate performances. Even mum's mitochondria and the genes which control heart size, muscle composition, and fat metabolism are only up to explaining about 30 per cent of the variation in performances in Great Britain, the United States, Timbuktu, and any where else.

The rest of the variation - about 70 per cent - is due to the environment, e.g., training and lifestyle factors. So, the next time you line up at the start of a race, remember that genes have indeed played a role in determining how long it will take you to get to the finish line but that your training and nutritional practices have had an even larger impact! That's good news, because it means that your destiny as an endurance athlete is to a great extent under your own control.

Nutrition for Infants (0-12 Months)

Good nutrition is essential for infants. Infants grow and develop faster during the first year of life than at any other time. For their size, infants require more calories and different types, textures, and portions of food for good health and proper growth.

Nutrient Needs

— *Calories*: Infants have higher calorie needs based on body weight than adults. Infants gain weight rapidly their first year. A healthy infant will double their birth weight by about five months of age and will triple their birth weight by about one year of age. In addition to a rapid growth rate, infants have a high metabolic rate, about twice that of an adult, based on body weight. After about six months, an infants' metabolic rate begins to decrease as growth rate slows down, but some of the calories saved by slower growth are used by increased activity.

— *Protein*: Adequate protein intake is critical for an infants' growth. Most infants who breastfeed or consume the recommended amounts of infant formula consume adequate protein. An infants' protein intake can exceed their need if they consume more formula than recommended or if food sources of protein such as infant cereal are added to infant formula. Infants can get too little or too much protein if infant formula is not made correctly, such as when too much or too little water is used in preparing infant formula powder or concentrate.

— *Fat*: Children under two years of age should not have fat limited in the diet. The dietary recommendation that fat intake should account for not more than 30% of calories is for adults and children over two years of age. Fat is an excellent source of calories that supports an infants' rapid growth. More than 50% of the calories in an infants' diet should come from fat. The type and amount of fat in breast milk and infant formula is right for an infant under one year of age.

— *Vitamins and Minerals*: Recommended vitamin and mineral intakes are based on the average amount of vitamins and minerals consumed by thriving infants' breastfed by well-nourished mothers. An infants' need for most vitamins and minerals, based on body weight, is more than double those of an adult.

— *Fluids*: Breast milk or formula generally provides adequate water for infants for the first four to six months. In hot, humid climates infants may need supplemental water, but water should not replace breast milk or formula. If supplemental water is provided, one to two ounces of water should be added after a normal feeding. For infants less than four months, water should be boiled first, chilled, and then offered in a sterilized bottle.

Replacing fluids is especially important for infants suffering from vomiting and/or diarrhea to prevent dehydration. Infants are not able to indicate if they are thirsty, especially when they are sick. Vomiting and diarrhea can result in dehydration more rapidly in infants than in older children. The loss of fluids also results in loss of electrolytes (sodium, potassium and chlorine). A physician may recommend the use of special fluids with contain electrolytes over plain water to replace fluids lost due to vomiting and diarrhea.

Infants' First Food

For the first four to six months an infants nutritional needs can be met by breast milk, infant formula or a combination of both. Breast milk or infant formula should continue throughout the first year of life. Breast milk is the best food for infants during the first year. Breast milk is specifically designed to meet the special nutritional needs of infants and is easily digested. Colostrum, which is secreted the first few days after birth, contains antibodies that can help protect infants against infections. Breastfeeding also enhances bonding between the mother and infant. Infant formulas are the best alternative to breast milk during the first year of life. Infant formulas are formulated to be like breast milk and provide all the nutrients an infant needs.

Cow's milk is not recommended as a substitute for breast milk or infant formula. Cow's milk is more difficult to digest, and the nutrients are not ideally balanced for infants. Cow's milk contains more protein, potassium and sodium than is recommended for infants and does not provide adequate amounts of iron, zinc, vitamin C, vitamin E and essential fatty acids for infants. Whole cow's milk can be fed to infants when breast milk and formula are no longer offered, usually when the infant turns one year of age.

Feeding Schedule

Newborn infants are not on a regular schedule. Newborn infant feedings are usually 1 ½ to 3 hours apart. Newborn infants may eat as little as one ounce or as much as four ounces at a single feeding. This is because newborn infants have small stomachs and need to be fed small amounts frequently. Eventually the time between feedings may lengthen to three or four hours.

For the first few days, breastfed infants nurse about ten minutes on each breast. Later, feedings increase to 10 to 20 minutes at each breast. Formula fed infants may eat two to three ounces at each feeding for the first week, increasing during the first month to two to six ounces per feeding.

Introducing Solid Foods

Through the first year, breast milk or infant formula should be the infants' main source of nutrients and calories. By four to six months infants are physically ready to begin solid foods. Breastfeeding or formula feeding should be continued throughout the first year, although the infant will probably drink less as more solid foods are added. Each infant is different and age is only a point of reference. The following signs may suggest the time is right to introduce solid foods:

— Infant can sit with little support.

— Infant shows interest in foods others are eating.

— Infant can move foods from the front to the back of the mouth.

— Infant can turn away to signal "enough."

There is no nutritional advantage to introducing solid food prior to four to six months of age. The main purpose of offering food on a spoon to infants at four to six months of age is to stimulate mouth muscle development, rather than providing nutrition, which, with the exception of iron, is met from breast milk or infant formula.

Watching for Food Allergies

The timing and spacing of introducing new foods is used to identify any food allergies. Recommendations are to introduce new single ingredient foods one at a time. Offer each new food for two or three days and then wait four to five days before introducing the next new food. If an allergic reaction such as a skin rash, digestive problems or respiratory discomfort occurs the food should be discontinued before introducing the next food.

The incidence of true food allergies is higher in younger than older children. About six to eight percent of children under four years of age have allergies that start in infancy. Foods that commonly cause allergic reactions in some infants includes wheat, shellfish, eggs, milk, tomato, citrus, peanuts and other nuts.

Most food allergies develop to the protein in a food, often following a gastrointestinal illness. Normally, protein is broken down during digestion so that groups of two or three amino acids linked together are absorbed. After an illness, small areas of irritated or inflamed intestinal lining may allow larger protein fragments to be absorbed. Such fragments are believed to trigger a reaction as if a foreign protein has invaded, setting up an immune or inflammatory response. The absorption of larger protein fragments is the basis for allergic reactions.

— *Infant Cereal*: Single grain infant cereals are usually the first solid foods introduced at four to six months. A full-term infant is born with an iron reserve that will last four to six months, at which time iron needs to be supplemented the infants' diets. Iron is usually supplemented at four to six months through the introduction of iron fortified infant cereals or iron fortified infant formula. Expressed breast milk or infant formula, not cows milk should be used to mix with infant cereals. Start with one teaspoon and gradually increase to two tablespoons once or twice a day. Sugar or honey should not be added to infant cereal. Do not put infant cereal in a bottle or infant feeder.

— *Fruits and Vegetables*: Fruits and vegetables are added to an infants' diet around six to eight months. Use plain, single-ingredient new infant fruits and vegetables. Start with one teaspoon and increase to one to two tablespoons per day. Sugar, salt, or margarine should not be added to infant fruits or vegetables.

Juices can also be introduced. However, only 100% pure juice should be offered. Juice should only be offered from a cup and servings should be limited to four ounces, because the sugar in juice can lead to dental caries. Citrus juices like orange and pineapple are usually delayed until one year of age. Juices should not be used as a substitute for breast milk or formula.

— *Meat, Poultry and Fish*: Meat, poultry and fish are added to an infants' diet at about eight to ten months of age. Tender strained infant meats should be introduced first. Start with one teaspoon and increase to one to two tablespoons per day. These provide older infants with other sources of iron. Salt should not be added to infant meats.

— *Eggs, Cheese and Yogurt*: Eggs, cheese and yogurt can be added at eleven to twelve months of age. Only egg yolk should be introduced. Because egg whites are often a cause of allergic reactions, whole eggs and egg whites are not introduced until an infant in one year of age. Never feed infants raw eggs because they can cause severe intestinal problems. Start with one teaspoon and increase until the infant takes the whole yolk daily. Plain yogurt or yogurt mixed with fruit can be introduced, but fruit yogurts that contain seeds should be avoided.

Servings by Ten to Twelve Months

— Breastfeed – on demand

— Infant Formula – three to four, eight ounce bottles daily

— Juice – four ounces daily (cup only)

— Cereal – four or more tablespoons, twice daily

— Vegetables – two or more tablespoons, twice daily

— Fruit – two or more tablespoons, twice daily

— Meat – two or more tablespoons, at least once daily

Cautions

It is not necessary to add salt, sugar or other seasonings to infant foods. Infants and toddlers less than two years of age should not be fed honey or corn syrup. Honey and corn syrup have been linked with infant botulism.

Homemade Baby Foods

Commercial baby foods are not required by infants. Parents can prepare baby foods at home using a blender or food processor, or by mashing with a fork. Care must be taken; however, to avoid contamination of home prepared baby foods by bacteria on food or from unsanitary storage methods.

Foods and Choking

During the transition from strained foods to regular table foods, choking is a major concern. The grinding action of a child's teeth is not very effective until at least four years of age. Because of this, foods that are hard or tough to chew, small and round or sticky are most often choked on. Many foods may cause choking unless the shape or texture can be modified. The following foods may cause choking and should be avoided.

— Hot dogs

— Tough stringy meats

— Chunks of meat

— Fish with bones

— Peanut butter

— Nuts

— Hard raw fruits (such as raw apple)

— Whole Grapes

— Hard raw vegetables (such as raw carrots)

— Whole beans

— Popcorn

— Small or hard candies

— Jelly beans

— Gum

— Gummy textured candies

Infant Dietary Supplements

Breastfed infants should be given a vitamin D supplement if exposure to sunlight is inadequate or if the mothers' diet does not include vitamin D fortified dairy foods. Adequate exposure to sunlight is defined as 30 minutes per week in just diapers or two hours per week in clothes but no hat.

A B_{12} supplement may be prescribed for breastfed infants if the mother is a vegan and does not eat meat or meat products.

An infants' prenatal iron storage becomes depleted around four to six months of age. Iron can be supplied from iron-fortified infant formula or iron-fortified infant cereal. Infants should not be supplemented with fluoride until six months of age. Thereafter, infants may need a fluoride supplement if the water has less than 0.3 parts per million (ppm) of fluoride.

Infant Tooth Decay

Frequent nursing at night after one year of age increases the risk for dental caries. Children who are nursed for long durations may develop dental caries between two to three years of age. Formula fed infants should not be put to bed with a bottle due to the increased risk of dental caries and choking.

Colic

Colic is the sudden onset of irritability or crying in young infants. Colic is often believed to be related to gastrointestinal problems. The relationship between colic, gastrointestinal problems and infant feeding practices has been studied, but no definite cause has been found. Colic episodes may have a similar pattern of onset during the day, and last about the same amount of time each day. Symptoms tend to disappear by three to four months of age. Recommendations to relieve coli may include rocking, swaddling, bathing, or other ways of calming the infant, positioning the infant well for eating or burping to relieve gas.

Infant Sensitivities

There is no basis for the concern that maternal intake of foods, such as cabbage or legumes, causing gas in breastfed infants. Large amounts of essential oils in foods such as garlic and spices can pass into breast milk and may alter the flavour, and occasionally breastfed infants may object to their presence. Some infants are sensitive to certain foods in the mother's diet. Garlic, onions, cabbage, turnips, broccoli, beans, rhubarb, apricots or prunes may be bothersome to some breastfed infants making them colicky for a day.

During the summer, large maternal intakes of melon, peaches and other fresh fruits may cause colic and diarrhea in breastfed infants. Red pepper has been reported to cause dermatitis in breastfed infants within an hour of feeding. Contrary to popular belief, chocolate rarely causes problems and can be consumed in moderation without causing colic, diarrhea or constipation in most breastfed infants.

Weaning

Developmental readiness for a cup begins at six to eight months. Eight month old infants enjoy trying to mimic drinking from open cups. However, the ability to elevate the tongue and control the liquid emerges later, closer to one year of age. Recommendations are to introduce a cup for water and juices about six to eight months of age so that by the time an infant is one year of age, and weaning from the breast or bottle is planned, the infant will be skilled enough at drinking from a cup to meet their fluid needs without a bottle. Infants are likely to decrease total calorie intake from breast milk or infant formula if a cup is used, since they are less efficient in the mouth skills needed. Typically weaning is accomplished by twelve to fourteen months of age.

Changing from a bottle to a covered sippy cup with a small spout is not the same developmental step as weaning to an open cup. The mouth skills in controlling liquids with the tongue are more advanced with an open cup. The mouth skills learned in drinking from an open cup also helps encourage speech development.

Overweight and Obesity

Weight loss is not appropriate in infancy. If an infant is classified as overweight or obese the emphasis is to stay close to the same weight until the infant grows taller. When an infant is overweight or obese it is more important to give a limited amount of regular formula (26 to 32 ounces per day) than to give larger amounts of diluted formula or skimmed milk. Regular formula has the nutrients needed for an infants' proper growth, feeding larger amounts of diluted formula still encourages an infant to overeat.

Skimmed milk is not appropriate for overweight or obese infants because it does not contain enough calories and may result in electrolyte imbalance. Juice contains nutrients, but is high in calories. Juice should be limited to three to four ounces per day and should not be offered until six to nine months of age.

— To help prevent obesity it is important to:

— Avoid overfeeding

— Do not force and infant to eat

— Wait until four to six months of age before introducing solid foods

— Limit juice to three to four ounces per day

— Do not use food as a reward

— Encourage physical activity even in infancy

Do not use food as a reward

Enjoy mealtime with toddlers. Don't nag about eating.

Nutrition for Toddlers (12-24 Months)

Adequate nutrition is necessary for toddlers to achieve their full growth and developmental potential.

Development of Feeding Skills in Toddlers

Motor development during the toddler years enhances their ability to chew food and to self-feed. At about twelve months, toddlers are able to grasp and pick up small objects such as cooked peas and carrots, and put them into their mouths. Increased motor and coordination skills allow toddlers to use cups and spoons, but not very well and they prefer to eat with their hands. Begging attempts at self-feeding are inevitably messy, but are an important step in development. Between twelve to eighteen months, toddlers learn to chew food with rotary, rather than just up and down movements. This ability allows toddlers to handle chopped or soft table food. From eighteen to twenty-four months, toddlers gain well-developed rotary chew movements. This ability allows toddlers to handle meats, raw fruits and vegetables and multiple textures.

Toddlers are easily distracted. It is important to keep distractions during meals, such as television, to a minimum. Mealtime is when toddlers need to practice self-feeding skills and to experience new foods and textures.

Introducing Whole Cows' Milk

Only breast milk or infant formula should be used until twelve months of age. After twelve months of age, whole cows' milk is recommended until twenty-four months of age. Use of low-fat milk or limiting other sources of dietary fat is not recommended for toddlers under two years of age. Toddlers need the calories from fat to fuel their rapid growth. Low-fat and skim milk do not provide enough calories to meet the high calorie needs of toddlers.

Transition to Regular Table Food

The diet for a toddler is a transition from pureed and strained foods to regular table foods. By twelve months of age toddlers have most of their baby teeth, and so foods with more texture and chewiness can be used. Junior baby foods have more texture and are a good transition between strained food and table foods. As new table foods are introduced the same guidelines should be used as when introducing strained baby foods. New foods should be added slowly and only one new food added at a time.

Finger foods such as pieces of banana, toasted oat ring cereals and small pieces of soft meat sticks can help in the transition from pureed foods to table foods. Snacks are an important part of a toddler's diet. Nutritious snacks such as fruits, juices, cheese or toddler crackers should be chosen instead of sweetened beverages, snack foods or desserts.

Nutrient Needs

— *Appetite*: During the toddler year's growth is slower than in infancy, which is often reflected by a lower appetite and interest in food. It is important for parents to understand that a decrease in appetite is normal at this age.

  Toddlers can regulate their calorie intake if they are allowed to choose how much to eat and when to stop eating. While the amount or food a toddler might eat at any given meal might not seem adequate over the course of time, toddlers are likely to eat sufficient calories.

— *Calories*: Calorie needs of toddlers reflect their decreased growth rate. The RDA for calories for one to three year olds is 102 calories/kg body weight.

— *Protein*: The RDA for protein for children one to six years of age is approximately 1.2 grams protein/kg body weight. This amount is easily met with a typical diet. Adequate calories have a protein sparing effect, in that when calories are adequate protein is used for growth and tissue repair instead of for energy. Intake of high-quality protein, such as milk and animal products, lowers the amount of dietary protein needed to provide the essential amino acids.

— *Fat*: Dietary fat intake should not be restricted for toddlers under two years of age. Toddlers need the calories from fat to fuel their rapid growth. Low-fat and skim milk do not provide enough calories to meet the high calorie needs of toddlers.

— *Vitamins and Minerals*: Dietary Reference Intakes (DRI's) and Recommended Dietary Allowances (RDA's) have been established for vitamins and minerals for toddlers. Based on nationwide surveys most children from birth to five years of age are meeting the recommended intake of most vitamins and minerals with the exception of iron, calcium and zinc. Recommended intakes for one to three year olds for iron is 7 mg/day, zinc 3 mg/day and calcium 500 mg/day.

— *Iron*: Iron continues to be a very important nutrient for toddlers. A rapid growth rate along with a frequently inadequate intake of iron places toddlers, especially nine to eighteen month olds, at the highest risk for iron deficiency. According to nationwide surveys 9% of toddlers aged one to two years are iron deficient and 3% have iron deficiency anemia. Continuing to feed toddlers iron-fortified cereals until two years of age can help reduce the risk of iron deficiency and anemia. In addition, the CDC recommends that children one to five years of age drink no more than 24 ounces of milk each day due to the low iron content. Larger intakes may displace intake of iron rich foods.

— *Calcium*: Adequate calcium intake in childhood affects peak bone mass, which protect against osteoporosis later in life. Many children do not consume enough calcium. An important aspect of adequate calcium intake during toddler years is the development of eating patterns that lead to adequate calcium intake later childhood.

— *Fiber*: Adequate dietary fiber helps prevent constipation in young children and is part of a healthy diet. Some of the best food sources of dietary fiber for toddlers are whole grain breads and cereals, fruits and vegetables appropriate for age. Too much fiber; however, should be avoided because toddlers can easily develop diarrhea from excessive fiber intake. In addition, excessive intake of high-fiber foods may decrease the intake of nutrient and energy-dense foods.

Food Guide Pyramid

Although toddlers can self-regulate calorie intake, there is no natural mechanism to direct them to choose a well-balanced diet. Children learn healthy eating habits. Providing a variety of foods from all the Food Guide Pyramid food groups every day is the best assurance of supplying the calories, vitamins, minerals and other nutrients growing toddlers need. Offering a variety of foods at an early age sets the stage for lifelong healthful eating habits.

The Food Guide Pyramid recommends at least 6 servings from the grain group, 3 servings from the vegetable group, 2 servings from the fruit group, 2 servings from the milk group and 2 servings from the meat group. Foods high in fats and sweets should be used in moderation.

Serving Sizes

Toddlers need toddler-sized servings. A rule of thumb for

servings is 1 tablespoon of food per year of age. It's better to give a toddler a small portion and allow them to ask for more than to provide large servings.

Meals and Snacks

Toddlers have small stomachs so they can't eat a large amount of food at one time. As a result snacks are important to meet their nutritional needs. It is important that snacks contribute nutrients to the whole days' intake. Toddlers should not be allowed to "graze" throughout the day on sweetened beverages, snack foods or desserts. These foods can hurt their limited appetite for basic foods at meals and snacks.

Toddlers need regular meal and snack times, allowing enough time between meals and snacks for the toddler to get hungry. Toddlers should be allowed to eat until they are full. It is unwise to force a toddler to eat or to use food as a reward.

Food Jags

The rapid growth rate beginning at conception tremendously slows down at around eighteen to twenty-four months of age causing many toddlers to change eating patterns. As toddlers become more independent, they enjoy feeding themselves and often develop their own food likes and dislikes. It is common for toddlers to go on food jags (eating the same food for weeks in a row) or food strikes (refusing to eat certain foods or any food at all). Toddlers may choose the same foods for one week and ignore them the next. Since food jags are usually short term, a toddlers' nutrient intake over time are balanced.

To overcome food jags, parents can serve new foods along with familiar foods. New foods are better accepted if they are served when the toddler is hungry and also if the toddler sees other family members eating these foods.

Mealtime with Toddlers

Mealtime is an opportunity for toddlers to practice language and social skills and to develop a positive self-image. Mealtime is not a time for battles over food or for "forced feeding."

Foods and Choking

During the transition from strained foods to regular table foods, choking is a major concern. The grinding action of a child's teeth is not very effective until at least four years of age. Because of this, foods that are hard or tough to chew, small and round or sticky are most often choked on. Many foods may cause choking unless the shape or texture can be modified. For example, peanut butter alone can cause choking. Thinning peanut butter with milk can reduce the risk of choking.

Another approach is to use a very thin layer of peanut butter of toast instead of bread to encourage chewing. Hot dogs, grapes and other raw fruits and vegetables need to be cut into very small pieces. Avoid circular shapes with hot dogs and carrots. Circular shapes are easier to choke on these foods need to be cut into half-moon shapes or even smaller. The following foods may cause choking and should be avoided unless the shape or texture can be modified.

— Hot dogs

— Tough stringy meats

— Chunks of meat

— Fish with bones

— Peanut butter

— Nuts

— Hard raw fruits (such as raw apple)

— Whole grapes

— Hard raw vegetables (such as raw carrots)

— Whole beans

— Popcorn

— Small or hard candies

— Jelly beans

— Gum

— Gummy textured candies

Whenever toddlers eat they should be sitting upright, not lying down or running around. Always supervise at snack and meal times because a child who is choking cannot make noise to attract your attention.

Food Allergies

Foods and beverages can cause reactions, although they are not common. Food allergies can occur at any age, but they are most common among infants and toddlers. Some symptoms of food allergies are runny, itchy nose and eyes, hives, dermatitis, asthma, stuffy nose and eczema. A food allergy may be suspected if a toddler develops any of these symptoms after eating a specific food.

Vitamin and Mineral Supplements

Children who consume a variety of foods from all the Food Guide Pyramid food groups can meet their nutritional needs without taking vitamin or mineral supplements. Eating a variety of foods is the best way to get all the nutrients needed, because foods contain many other substances in addition to vitamins and minerals.

Tooth Decay

A primary cause of tooth decay is continual use of a bottle with milk or fruit juice at bedtime or through the day. Prolonged exposure of the teeth to these fluids can produce baby bottle tooth decay. Upper front teeth are the most severely affected by decay, which is where fluids pool when toddlers fall asleep while drinking from a bottle.

Foods containing carbohydrates that stick to the surface of the teeth can also promote tooth decay. Rinsing the mouth with water or brushing teeth to get rid of the carbohydrate stuck to the teeth reduces tooth decay. The risk of tooth decay also increases the more time the teeth are exposed to carbohydrate. Not allowing toddlers to continually eat or drink throughout the day can reduce the amount of time the teeth are exposed to carbohydrate and can decrease the risk of tooth decay.

To help prevent tooth decay, children need a source of fluoride in the diet. Children six months to six years of age may need additional fluoride if their local water supply has less than 0.3 ppm fluoride.

Constipation

Constipation is a common problem among toddlers. Diets providing adequate fiber appropriate for the child's age can help protect against constipation. Adequate fluid intake is also important to protect against constipation.

Overweight and Obesity

Weight loss is not appropriate for toddlers. Adequate nutrients must be provided for normal growth and development. If a toddler is classified as overweight or obese the emphasis is to stay close to the same weight until the toddler grows taller. To help prevent obesity it is important to:

— Avoid overfeeding

— Do not force a toddler to eat

— Encourage physical activity

— Time meals and snacks at approximately the same time every day

— Use appropriate serving sizes

— Choose snacks carefully

— Limit intake of juice. Although juice provides nutrients it is high in calories

— Do not use food as a reward

— Enjoy mealtime with toddlers. Don't nag about eating.

Nutrition for Young Children (2 – 6 Years)

Adequate nutrition is necessary for young children to achieve their full growth and developmental potential.

Development of Feeding Skills in Young Children

The young child can use a fork, spoon and cup fairly well. However, the ability to spread or cut is usually still difficult. Eating is not a messy for young children as it is for toddlers. However, accidents and spills still occur, but they are not intentional.

Nutrient Needs

— *Appetite*: As during the toddler year's, growth is slower for young children than in infancy, which is reflected by a lower appetite and interest in food. It is important for parents to understand that a decrease in appetite is normal at this age. Appetite and food intake tends to increase in advance of a growth spurt, causing young children to gain some weight that will be used for an upcoming spurt in growth.

  An important aspect of nutrition for young children is a young child's ability to self-regulate food intake. If allowed to decide when to eat and when to stop eating without outside interference, young children will eat as much as they need. Young children have an innate ability to adjust calorie intake to meet their calorie needs. Young children's food intake may fluctuate widely from meal to meal and day to day; however, over a week's time, young children's calorie intake remains fairly stable. Forcing a young child to eat or using food as a reward can cause a young child to lose their ability to self-regulate food intake and detect satiety cues.

— *Calories*: The RDA for calories for one to three year olds is 102 calories/kg body weight. The RDA for calories for four to six year olds is 90 calories/kg body weight. The decrease in the RDA for calories with age reflects the decrease in growth rate.

— *Protein*: The RDA for protein for children one to six years of age is approximately 1.2 grams protein/kg body weight. This amount is easily met with a typical diet. Adequate calories have a protein sparing effect, in that when calories are adequate protein is used for growth and tissue repair instead of for energy. Intake of high-quality protein, such as milk and animal products, lowers the amount of dietary protein needed to provide the essential amino acids.

— *Fat*: The American Academy of Pediatrics does not advise restriction of fat during the first two years. However, after two years of age, the American Academy of Pediatrics recommends children gradually adopt a diet that by the age of 5 years reflects the following pattern:

— Total fat not more than 30% and not less than 20% of total calories

— Saturated fat less than 10% of total calories

— Dietary cholesterol less than 300 mg/day

The American Academy of Pediatrics cautions against restriction of meat and dairy products, as a way to lower fat intake, because they serve as the primary dietary sources of protein, iron and calcium, as well as other essential nutrients needed for growth and development.

— *Vitamins and Minerals*: Dietary Reference Intakes (DRI's) and Recommended Dietary Allowances (RDA's) have been established for vitamins and minerals for young children. Based on nationwide surveys most children from birth to five years of age are meeting the recommended intake of most vitamins and minerals with the exception of iron, calcium and zinc. Recommended intakes are:

Age	Iron (mg/d)	Zinc (mg/d)	Calcium (mg/d)
1-3 Years	7	3	500
4-8 Years	10	5	800

— *Iron*: Iron deficiency and iron deficiency anemia are prevalent nutrition problems among young children in the United States. Rapid growth combined with low iron intake places young children at risk for iron deficiency. The CDC recommends children one to five years of age drink no more than 24 ounces of milk each day due to the low iron content. Larger intakes may displace intake of iron rich foods.

— *Calcium*: Adequate calcium intake in childhood affects peak bone mass, which protect against osteoporosis later in life. Many children do not consume enough calcium. An important aspect of adequate calcium intake early years is the development of eating patterns that lead to adequate calcium intake later childhood.

— *Fiber*: Adequate dietary fiber helps prevent constipation in young children and is part of a healthy diet. Some of the best food sources of dietary fiber for young children are whole grain breads and cereals, fruits and vegetables appropriate for age. Too much fiber; however, should be avoided because young children can easily develop diarrhea from excessive fiber intake. In addition, excessive intake of high-fiber foods may decrease the intake of nutrient and energy-dense foods.

A reasonable dietary fiber intake for children three through twenty years of age is the sum of their age plus five. For example, a five year old child's dietary fiber goal would be 10 grams per day.

Food Guide Pyramid for Young Children

Although young children can self-regulate calorie intake, there is no natural mechanism to direct them to choose a well-balanced diet. Children learn healthy eating habits. Providing a variety of foods following the Food Guide Pyramid every day is the best assurance of supplying the calories, vitamins, minerals and other nutrients young children need.

The USDA developed a Food Guide Pyramid for Young Children, targeting children two to six years of age. The Food Guide Pyramid for Young Children encourages children to eat a variety of foods. Foods shown in the Food Guide Pyramid for Young Children represent single serving portions of foods commonly consumed by young children. To make the Food Guide Pyramid for Young Children "child friendly," the food groups have shorter names and a single number rather than a range is use for the number of food group servings. To emphasize the importance of physical activity, pictures of children being active are shown around the pyramid.

The Food Guide Pyramid recommends at least 6 servings from the grain group, 3 servings from the vegetable group, 2 servings from the fruit group, 2 servings from the milk group and 2 servings from the meat group. Foods high in fats and sweets should be used in moderation.

Serving Sizes

Four to six year olds can eat the serving sizes recommended by the Food Guide Pyramid for Young Children. Two to three year olds need the same number of serving as is recommended for four to six year olds, but serving sizes are about two-thirds for younger children, except for milk.

Recommended versus Actual Food Intake

Comparing young children's actual food intake to the number of servings recommended by the Food Guide Pyramid reveals that the average number of food group servings for children ages 2 to 5 years of age are below minimum recommendations for all food groups except for the dairy group, which is at or near recommended intakes.

Most young children meet calorie intake recommendations. The average distribution of calories for young children 3 to 5 years of age is 54% from carbohydrates, 14% from protein and 32% from fat, of which 12% is from saturated fat.

Snacks

Snacking among young children makes important contributions to total calorie and nutrient takes.

Young children have small stomachs so they can't eat a large amount of food at one time. As a result snacks are important to meet their nutritional needs. It is important that snacks contribute nutrients to the whole days' intake. Young children should not be allowed to "graze" throughout the day on sweetened beverages, snack foods or desserts. These foods can hurt their limited appetite for basic foods at meals and snacks.

Snack suggestions

— Bananas dipped in fruit or yogurt.

— Bread or Toast spread with cream cheese or spreadable cheese.

— Quick Breads or Muffins made with carrots, zucchini, pumpkin, bananas, lemons, and berries.

— Flour Tortillas spread with refried beans, sprinkled with grated cheese and broiled and cut into fourths.

- Pita Bread filled with sliced meat, cheese, lettuce and tomato.
- English Muffins topped with spaghetti sauce, grated cheese, broiled and cut into fourths.
- Potato Skins sprinkled with shredded cheese and broiled.
- Canned Chili heated and used as a dip for French bread cubes or corn bread.
- Parfait made with yogurt, fruit and granola.
- Gelatin made with added fruit, grated carrots, or cottage cheese.
- Frozen Fruit Cubes made by freezing purred applesauce or fruit juice in ice cube trays.
- Fruit Fizz made by adding club soda to fruit juice.
- Fruit Shake made by blending milk with fresh fruit (bananas, berries, or peaches).
- Hot Chocolate made with cocoa and milk.
- Crackers served with spreadable cheese or cream cheese.
- Fruit Smoothies, yogurt, fresh fruit, and ice blended until smooth

Additional snack suggestions for older children

(These snacks are appropriate for children ages 4 and older. They may present a choking hazard for younger children).

- Fresh Vegetables served with a dip of cottage cheese or yogurt.
- Celery spread with either cream cheese, peanut butter, or spreadable cheese and topped with raisins or shredded carrots.
- Sliced Apples served with peanut butter or cream cheese.

Picky eaters

Young children are often described as being picky eaters. One reason young children may want the same foods all of the time is because familiar foods are comforting to a child. Another reason is children may be trying to have control over this part of their life.

One of the most important things you can teach a child at this age is to try a variety of foods. Every child is unique with his or her set of food likes and dislikes. There are some things to remember that will help a child eat a variety of foods, enjoy them, and be willing to try new ones. Mealtime should not be a battleground and forcing a child to eat food does not teach good habits. Some practical suggestions for young children include:

— Start with just a small spoonful or two

— Introduce new foods along with old favourites

— Use child-sized servings

— Serving food attractively

-- Young children often do not like foods to touch or to be mixed together

— Young children typically don't like strongly flavored or spicy foods

— Don't allow young children to eat and drink indiscriminately between meals and snacks. This often "kills" an appetite at mealtime.

— Don't force a child to stay at the table until they have eaten a certain amount of food.

Mealtime with Young Children

Mealtime is an opportunity for young children to practice language and social skills and to develop a positive self-image. Mealtime is not a time for battles over food or for "forced feeding."

Foods and Choking

The grinding action of a child's teeth is not very effective until at least four years of age. Because of this, foods that are hard or tough to chew, small and round or sticky are most often choked on.

Many foods may cause choking unless the shape or texture can be modified. For example, peanut butter alone can cause choking. Thinning peanut butter with milk can reduce the risk of choking. Another approach is to use a very thin layer of peanut butter of toast instead of bread to encourage chewing. Hot dogs, grapes and other raw fruits and vegetables need to be cut into very small pieces. Avoid circular shapes with hot dogs and carrots. Circular shapes are easier to choke on these foods need to be cut into half-moon shapes or even smaller. Whenever young children eat they should be sitting upright, not lying down or running around. Always supervise at snack and meal times because a child who is choking cannot make noise to attract your attention.

The following foods may cause choking and should be avoided unless the shape or texture can be modified.

— Hot dogs

— Tough stringy meats

— Chunks of meat

— Fish with bones

— Peanut butter

— Nuts

— Hard raw fruits (such as raw apple)

— Whole grapes

— Hard raw vegetables (such as raw carrots)

— Whole beans

— Popcorn

— Small or hard candies
— Jelly beans
— Gum
— Gummy textured candies

Vitamin and Mineral Supplements

Children who consume a variety of foods from all the Food Guide Pyramid food groups can meet their nutritional needs without taking vitamin or mineral supplements. Eating a variety of foods is the best way to get all the nutrients needed, because foods contain many other substances in addition to vitamins and minerals.

Tooth Decay

Foods containing carbohydrates that stick to the surface of the teeth can also promote tooth decay. Rinsing the mouth with water or brushing teeth to get rid of the carbohydrate stuck to the teeth reduces tooth decay. The risk of tooth decay also increases the more time the teeth are exposed to carbohydrate. Not allowing young children to continually eat or drink throughout the day can reduce the amount of time the teeth are exposed to carbohydrate and can decrease the risk of tooth decay.

To help prevent tooth decay, children need a source of fluoride in the diet. Children six months to six years of age may need additional fluoride if their local water supply has less than 0.3 ppm fluoride.

Constipation

Constipation is a common problem among young children. Diets providing adequate fiber appropriate for the child's age can help protect against constipation. Adequate fluid intake is also important to protect against constipation.

Overweight and Obesity

Weight loss is not appropriate for young children between two to seven years of age. Adequate nutrients must be provided for normal growth and development. If a young child is classified as overweight or obese the emphasis is to stay close to the same weight until the child grows taller.

Inactivity is thought to be a major contributor to the increasing incidence of obesity. The Dietary Guidelines for Americans recommend young children participate in at least 60 minutes every day. To help prevent obesity it is important to:

- — Avoid overfeeding
- — Do not force a child to eat
- — Time meals and snacks at approximately the same time every day
- — Use appropriate serving sizes
- — Choose snacks carefully
- — Limit intake of juice. Although juice provides nutrients it is high in calories
- — Do not use food as a reward
- — Encourage young children to be physically active
- — Limit the time young children watch television and play computer games

Involve Young Children

Young children want to be helpful and to please their parents and caregivers. This makes young childhood a good time to teach children about foods, food selection and preparation by involving them in simple food related activities.

Children as young as 2 years or age can be encouraged to help prepare meals. They can stir goods and slice soft foods with a table knife. As their interest and abilities increase children can take a more active role in meal planning, food buying and preparation. Children may even enjoy growing some garden foods. Following cookbooks can help children read and follow directions. Children can be involved in setting the table, serving and cleaning up. Such responsibilities are part of growing up.

Children involved in meal preparation develop a more active interest in food. They can accomplish many different tasks when working one-on-one with an adult in the kitchen. Having patience and time to spend with children when involving them in meal preparation is the key to success. If you would like to involve children in food preparation, be sure to:

— Supervise all activities.

— Match the task to the child's capabilities.

— Provide detailed instructions, demonstrations and time for practice.

— Repeat instructions before a child begins to perform a task.

— Incorporate cleanup as part of each job.

— Have children stand on steady stools to perform some task.

Nutrition for Adolescence (11 – 21 Years)

Adolescence, in general, is defined as the period between 11 and 21 years of age. It is a time of dramatic biological, psychological, social and mental change, in which a child develops into an adult.

The dramatic changes that occur during adolescence affect nutritional needs. The dramatic physical growth and development that occurs during adolescents significantly increase calorie, protein, vitamin and mineral requirements. However, the struggle for independence that occurs with psychological and social development often leads health-compromising eating behaviours, such as fad dieting and meal skipping.

Growth and Development

Almost half of adult body weight is gained during adolescence. In addition, almost half of adult peak bone mass is developed during adolescence.

Among females, peak weight gain follows the linear growth spurt by three to six months, and occurs at an average age of 12.5 years. Weight gain slows around the time of menarche, but continues into late adolescence. Peak muscle mass development for females occurs around or just after the onset of menarche. Body composition dramatically changes for females during adolescence. Average lean body mass decreases and average body fat increases from 16% to 27%. For females, body fat levels peak between the ages of 15 to 16 years. Research indicates a 17% body fat level is required for menarche to occur and a 25% body fat level is required for the development and maintenance of regular cycles.

Even though the accumulation of body fat by females is normal and physiologically necessary, adolescent females often view it negatively. Weight dissatisfaction is common among adolescent females during and immediately following puberty, increasing the risk of health compromising behaviours such as excessive dieting and calorie restriction, meal skipping, and in comes cases the development of a distorted body image and eating disorders. Among males, peak weight gain coincides with peak linear growth and peak muscle mass development.

Average body fat levels in males during adolescence decrease to an average of 12% by the end of puberty. By age 18, more than 90% of adult bone mass has been formed. A variety of factors affect the development of bone mass, including genetics, hormones, weight-bearing exercise, cigarette smoking, alcohol intake, and dietary intake of calcium, vitamin D, protein, phosphorus, boron and iron. Because bone is primarily composed of calcium, phosphorus, and protein and because a great deal of bone mass is developed during adolescence, adequate intake of these nutrients is crucial to promote peak bone mass development.

Eating Behaviours

Adolescent eating behaviours are influenced by many factors, including peers, parents, food availability, food preferences, cost, convenience, cultural, mass media and body image. Adolescents lead busy lives. Increasing school and personal activities, combined with an increased need for social contact and peer approval, leave little time for adolescents to sit down for meals. Snacking is common among adolescents. Snacks account for one-fourth to one-third of adolescents' daily calorie intake. Nationwide surveys report the proportion of calories from snacks has risen over the past decade.

Unfortunately, adolescent snack food choices tend to be high in sugar, sodium and fat, and low in vitamins and minerals. Soft drinks are the most commonly chosen snack by adolescent females. Skipping meals also increases during adolescence. Breakfast is the most common meal skipped. Only one-third of adolescent females tend to eat breakfast daily. Skipping breakfast can dramatically decrease intake of calories, protein, fiber, calcium and folate. Lunch is skipped by almost one-fourth of adolescents. As with breakfast, skipping lunch reduces intake of calories, protein, and other nutrients.

As adolescents grow and develop, they spend less time with their families and more time with their peers, and meals eaten away from home increases. In particular, eating at fast-food restaurants accounts for almost one-third of all food eaten away from home. Eating at fast-food restaurants can directly affect adolescents' nutrient intake. Many fast foods are high in fat and low in fiber and nutrients. However, adolescents' can make specific choices to increase the nutrient content of fast-food meals and decrease the fat content.

Dietary Intake

Many adolescents do not consume diets that provide the recommended number of servings following the Food Guide Pyramid. Nationwide surveys indicate only 1% of adolescents consume diets that meet recommendations for all the Food Guide Pyramid food groups, and only 5% meet recommendations for at least four Food Guide Pyramid food groups. Approximately, half of adolescents meet recommendations for one of the Food Guide Pyramid food groups, while 7% of adolescent males and 18% of adolescent females do not meet any recommendations for the Food Guide Pyramid food groups. Inadequate consumption of diary products, grain products, fruits and vegetables is common among adolescents.

Nationwide surveys indicate many adolescents consume inadequate amounts of vitamins and minerals, particularly among female adolescents. This is not surprising, given that most adolescents do not consume diets that comply with the Food Guide Pyramid. On average, adolescents consume diets inadequate in several vitamins and minerals including folate, vitamins A, B6, and E, iron, zinc and calcium. Dietary fiber intake among adolescents is also low. In addition, diets consumed by many adolescents exceed current recommendations for total and saturated fats, cholesterol, sodium and sugar.

Nutrient Needs

The increases in muscle mass, bone mass, and body fat that occurs during adolescence results in increased calorie and nutrient needs. Adolescent calorie and nutrient needs actually depend on the degree of physical development that has occurred. The Dietary Reference Intakes (DRI's) provide the best estimate of nutrient requirements for adolescents. However, it should be pointed out that the DRI's based on chronological age, rather than the level of individual physical development.

Calories

Adolescent calorie needs are affected by increased requirements to support growth and development, activity level and basal metabolic rate. The basal metabolic rate is closely related to the amount of muscle mass, because muscle has a higher metabolic rate than body fat. Because adolescent males have a greater increase in height, weight and muscle mass, they have a significantly higher calorie requirement than females. The RDA's for total calories by age group are listed below.

	Age	Calories/day
Females	11 – 14	2,200
	15 – 18	2,200
	19 – 24	2,200
Males	11 – 14	2,500
	15 – 18	3,000
	19 – 24	2,900

Due to the great variation in the timing of growth and development in adolescents, calculating calorie needs based on height provide better estimates of calorie needs. Approximately 99% of adolescent males and 86% of adolescent females meet or exceed the DRI for calories.

The DRI for calories is based on light to moderate activity level. Therefore, adolescents who participate in sports, those who are in training to increase muscle mass, and those who are more active than average may require additional calories to meet their specific needs. Conversely, adolescents who are not physically active or those who have a physical condition that limits their activity may require fewer calories to meet their specific needs.

Physical activity has been found to decrease throughout adolescence, with approximately one-fourth of adolescents involved in no physical activity. Therefore, calorie needs of older adolescents who have completed puberty and are less active may be significantly lower than those of younger, active, still-growing adolescents.

Physical growth and development during adolescence is affected by calorie and nutrient intakes. When calorie intake fails to meet requirements, linear growth may be decreased and sexual maturation may be delayed. The standard way to assess if calorie intake is adequate is to measure height, weight and body composition. If, over time, height and weight-for-height continuously fail within the same growth percentiles, it can be assumed that calorie needs are being met. If the percentile for weight-for-height begins to fall or rise, calorie intake should be assessed and calorie intake adjustments should be made accordingly.

Protein

Adolescent protein needs are affected by the amount of protein needed to maintaining muscle mass as well as the amount of protein required to build additional muscle mass during the adolescent growth spurt. Because protein needs vary with the amount of growth and development, requirements based on developmental age are more accurate than recommendations based on chronological age. Recommended protein intakes based upon age and gender are listed below.

	Age	Protein grams/day
Females	11 – 14	46
	15 – 18	44
	19 – 24	46
Males	11 – 14	45
	15 – 18	59
	19 – 24	58

Protein requirements are highest for females 11 to 14 years of age and for males 15 to 18 years of age. These peak periods of protein need correspond to the usual timing of peak height velocity. As with calories, growth is affected by protein intake. When protein intake is consistently inadequate, linear growth and muscle mass development may be decreased.

Typically, adolescents consume more than adequate amounts of protein. Nationwide surveys indicate that on average adolescents consume about two times the recommended level of protein intake. However, certain sub-groups of adolescents may be at risk for marginal or low protein intakes.

Carbohydrate

Carbohydrate is the body's primary source of calories. Carbohydrate rich foods, such as fruit, vegetables, grains, and legumes are also the main source of dietary fiber. Absolute requirements for carbohydrate intake among adolescents have not been established. However, dietary recommendations suggest that 50% or more of total calories should come from carbohydrate, with no more than 10% of calories from sweeteners, such as sucrose and high fructose corn syrup.

Nationwide surveys indicate adolescents consume approximately 53% of their calories from carbohydrate. Foods that contribute the most carbohydrate in adolescents' diets include yeast bread, soft drinks, milk, ready-to-eat cereal, and foods such as cakes, cookies, quick breads, donuts, sugars, syrups and jams. Sweeteners and added sugars provide approximately 16% of total calories in adolescents' diets. Soft drinks are a major source of added sugar in adolescents' diets, contributing more than 12% of all carbohydrate consumed. Estimates are 86% of all soft drinks adolescents consume are sweetened, non-diet soft drinks.

Fiber

Dietary fiber is important for normal bowel function and may play a role in the lowering the risk of certain cancers, heart disease and type 2 diabetes. Adequate fiber intake is thought to have a role in lowering blood cholesterol levels and moderating blood sugar levels. Recommended fiber intake for adolescents is based on an "age plus five" rule, where the adolescent's age is added to 5 to determine minimum fiber intake.

A factor of 10 is added to age to determine the recommended upper limit of fiber intake. Thus, a 14 year-old would require 19-24 grams of fiber each day. This rule of thumb corresponds to the American Academy of Pediatrics recommendation that adolescents' dietary fiber intake should be 0.5 grams per kilogram of body weight. This corresponds to an average fiber intake of 15.5 to 34.5 grams per day for 10 to 18 year old males and 16.0 to 28.5 grams per day for 10 to 18 year old females.

The American Academy of Pediatrics further recommendations that fiber intake should not exceed 35 grams per day, because levels above this amount may reduce the bioavailability of some minerals. Nationwide surveys indicate that adolescent males consume 11.5 to 15.4 grams of fiber each day and female adolescents consume 10.0 to 14.0 grams of fiber each day, which are below recommended fiber intake levels.

Significant sources of fiber in adolescents' diets include breads, ready-to-eat cereal, potatoes, popcorn and related snack foods, tomatoes and corn. Adolescents' low intake of fruit and vegetables is the greatest contributing factor to adolescent's low fiber intake. Adolescents who skip breakfast or do not routinely consume whole grain breads or ready-to-eat cereals are at high risk of not having an adequate fiber intake.

Fat

Dietary fat and essential fatty acids are required by the body for normal growth and development. Current recommendations for children over five year of age are to consume no more than 30% of total calories from fat, with no more than 10% of total calories from saturated fat, and no more than 300 milligrams of cholesterol per day. Nationwide surveys indicate that adolescents consume approximately 33% of total calories from fat, with approximately 12% from saturated fat.

Calcium

An adequate calcium intake is critical during adolescence because about half of peak bone mass is developed during this time. Adequate calcium intake during adolescence can result in the development of optimal bone mass and can reduce the risk of fractures and osteoporosis in later life. Adolescent females have the greatest calcium absorption rates around the time of menarche, after which calcium absorption rates decrease. Male calcium absorption rates also peak during early adolescence, a few years later than in females. Young adolescents have been found to retain four times more calcium than young adults. By 24 years of age in females and 26 years of age in males, calcium accumulation in bone mass is almost non-existent. This clearly indicates the importance of adequate calcium intake during adolescence.

The DRI for calcium for 9 to 18 year olds is 1,300 milligrams per day. Nationwide surveys indicate many adolescents, particularly females, do not consume adequate calcium. Adolescent females consume 536 to 815 milligrams of calcium per day, while adolescent males consume 681 to 1146 milligrams of calcium per day. These levels of calcium intake are not adequate to support the development of optimal bone mass. Supplements may be necessary for adolescents who do not consume adequate dietary calcium.

Milk provides the greatest amount of calcium in adolescents' diets, followed by cheese, ice cream and frozen yogurt. However, adolescents are increasingly consuming calcium from fortified foods. One study indicated that more than half of adolescents reported drinking calcium-fortified juices and approximately one-third ate calcium fortified cereals.

The consumption of soft drinks by adolescents may displace the consumption of more nutrient-dense beverages, including milk and fortified juices. Studies have showed an inverse relationship between carbonated beverage intake and milk and juice intake.

Calcium intake decreases with age among both male and female adolescents. However, adolescent males have a greater calcium intake at all ages than do adolescent females. Adolescent calcium intake is highly related to calorie intake. This suggests that adolescents, in particular females, who are restricting calories in an effort to control weight, are at particularly high risk for inadequate calcium intakes.

Iron

Adolescents' need for iron increases due to the rapid rate of linear growth, the increase in blood volume and the onset of menarche. Although the prevalence of iron deficiency anemia is relatively low among adolescents, a large proportion of adolescents have been reported to have inadequate iron stores. The DRI's for iron are:

	Age	Iron mg/day
Females	9 – 13	8
	14 – 18	15
	19 – 30	18
Males	9 – 13	8
	14 – 18	11
	19 – 30	8

The DRI's for iron are based on the amount of dietary iron needed to maintain a suitable iron storage level, to cover the rapid linear growth and onset of menstruation that occurs in females. Adolescent iron needs are the highest during the adolescent growth spurt in males and after the onset of menarche in females. Nationwide surveys indicate that approximately 30% of male and 80% of female adolescents do not consume the DRI for iron. The most common dietary sources of iron in adolescent's diets are ready-to-eat cereal, bread, and beef.

The two types of dietary iron are heme iron, which is found in animal products, and nonheme iron which is found in both animal and plant-based foods. The absorption and utilization of iron by the body is affected by its type. The bioavailability of heme iron is much greater than nonheme. However, the bioavailability of nonheme iron can be increased by consuming it with sources of heme iron or vitamin C.

Zinc

Zinc is particularly important during adolescence because of its role in RNA and protein synthesis and its role as a cofactor in over 200 enzymes. The body's need for zinc, along with its ability to retain zinc, dramatically increases during the adolescent growth spurt. Zinc is also required for sexual maturation. The bioavailability of zinc from dietary sources is highly dependant upon the source of zinc. Zinc from animal sources is more available than from plant based sources.

Dietary fiber in many plant based food sources of zinc can inhibit its absorption by the body. In addition, zinc and iron compete for absorption, so increased intakes of one can reduce the absorption of the other. Adolescents who take iron supplements may be at increased risk of developing mild zinc deficiency if iron intake is more than twice as high as that of zinc.

Nationwide surveys indicate that approximately 75% of male and 90% of female adolescents do not consume the DRI for zinc. The most common food sources of zinc in adolescents' diets include beef, milk, ready-to-eat-cereal, cheese, and poultry. The DRI's for zinc are:

	Age	Zinc mg/day
Females	9 – 13	8
	14 – 18	9
	19 – 30	8
Males	9 – 13	8
	14 – 18	11
	19 – 30	11

Folate

Folate has important roles in DNA, RNA, and protein synthesis. Thus, adolescents have increased needs for folate. Folate in the form of folic acid is twice as available as other forms of folate. For this reason, dietary folate equivalents (DFE's) are used in the DRI's. One microgram of folic acid is equivalent to approximately 2 DFE's, while 1 microgram of other forms of folate is equivalent to 1 DFE. Folic acid is the form of folate added to fortified cereals, breads, and other refined grain products. The DRI for folate for adolescent males and females are:

	Age	Folate ug/day
Females	9 – 13	300
	14 – 18	400
	19 – 30	400
Males	9 – 13	300
	14 – 18	400
	19 – 30	400

Severe folate deficiency can result in the development of megaloblastic anemia, which is rare among adolescents. However, surveys indicate that a significant proportion of adolescents have an inadequate folate status. Nationwide surveys indicate that many adolescents do not have an adequate folate intake. Approximately 25% of male and 40% of female adolescents do not consume the DRI for folate.

A poor dietary folate status among adolescent females can present an important issue related to reproduction. Studies show that an adequate folate intake prior to pregnancy can reduce the risk of spina bifida and other neural tube defects in the fetus. The protective effects of folate occur early in pregnancy often before a woman knows she is pregnant. Thus, it is critical that all women of reproductive age have an adequate folate intake, preferably through dietary sources, or it need be through supplements. The most common food sources of folate in adolescents' diets include ready-to-eat cereal, orange juice, bread, milk and dried beans or lentils. The low intake of fruits consumed by adolescents contributes to their low folate intake.

Vitamin A

Vitamin A deficiency is rare among adolescents; however, nationwide surveys have consistently reported low dietary intakes of vitamin A. It has been reported that approximately 50% of male and 60% of female adolescents do not consume the DRI for vitamin A. The most common food sources of vitamin A in adolescents' diets include ready-to-eat cereal, milk, carrots, margarine, and cheese. Beta-carotene, a precursor to vitamin A, is most commonly consumed by adolescents from carrots, tomatoes, spinach and other greens, sweet potatoes, and milk. The low intake of fruits, vegetables, milk, and dairy products by adolescents contributes to their low vitamin A intake.

Vitamin A recommendations are expressed as retinol activity equivalents (RAE). The DRI's for vitamin A are:

	Age	Vitamin A ug/day
Females	9 – 13	8
	14 – 18	15
	19 – 30	18

Males	9 – 13	8
	14 – 18	11
	19 – 30	8

Vitamin E

Vitamin E is well known for its antioxidant properties, a role that becomes increasingly important as body mass increases during adolescence. Nationwide surveys indicate that 65% of adolescent males and females do not consume the DRI for vitamin E. The most common food sources of vitamin E in adolescents' diets include margarine, salad dressings, mayonnaise, nuts/seeds, and tomatoes. The DRI's for vitamin E for are:

	Age	Vitamin E mg/day
Females	9 – 13	11
	14 – 18	15
	19 – 30	15
Males	9 – 13	11
	14 – 18	15
	19 – 30	15

Vitamin C

Vitamin C has a role in the synthesis of collagen and other connective tissues. Due to these functions, vitamin C has an important role during adolescent growth and development. Nationwide surveys indicate that adolescent vitamin C intakes are marginally adequate. The most common food sources of vitamin C in adolescents' diets are orange and grapefruit juice, fruit drinks, ready-to-eat cereals, tomatoes and white potatoes. The DRI's for vitamin C are:

	Age	Vitamin C mg/day
Females	9 – 13	45
	14 – 18	65

	19 – 30	75
Males	9 – 13	45
	14 – 18	75
	19 – 30	90

Food Guide Pyramid

Providing a variety of foods following the Food Guide Pyramid is the best way to ensure adolescents obtain the variety of nutrients they need everyday. The Food Guide Pyramid is an outline of what to eat each day. The Food Guide Pyramid calls for a variety of foods to get the nutrients you need. The Food Guide Pyramid recommends at 6-11 servings from the bread, cereal, rice, and pasta group each day, 3-5 servings daily from the vegetable group and 2-4 servings each day from the fruit group. Two to three servings each day are recommended from the milk, yogurt, and cheese group, and 2-3 servings daily are recommended from meat, poultry, fish, dry beans, eggs and nut group. Food high in fats, oils, and sweets are to be used in moderation.

Serving Sizes

Food Groups	Food Guide Pyramid Serving Sizes
Bread and Cereals	
Bread	1 slice
Cooked rice or pasta	1/2 C
Cooked cereal	1/2 C
Ready to eat cereal	1 ounce
Vegetables	
Cooked, chopped raw vegetables	1/2 C
Raw leafy vegetables	1 C
Fruits	
Fresh fruit	1 piece or wedge

Juice	3/4 C
Canned fruit	1/2 C
Dried fruit	1/4 C
Meat and Alternatives	
Lean meat, poultry or fish	2-3 oz
The following counts as 1 oz	
Cooked dry beans	1/2 C
Egg	1
Peanut butter	2 T
Milk	
Milk	1 C
Cheese	2 oz

Dietary Supplements

Adolescents who consume a variety of foods from all the Food Guide Pyramid food groups can meet their nutritional needs without taking vitamin or mineral supplements. Eating a variety of foods is the best way to get all the nutrients needed, because foods contain many other substances in addition to vitamins and minerals. However, as previously mentioned many adolescents do not do so.

Nationwide surveys indicate 15% to 30% of adolescents consume vitamin and/or mineral supplements. More than half of adolescents who report using vitamin and/or mineral supplements take them occasionally, with slightly less than half using them daily. Interestingly, adolescents who take vitamin and/or mineral supplements tend to consume a more nutritionally adequate diet than those who don't.

Adolescents who take vitamin and/or mineral supplements consume a smaller proportion of calories from total and saturated fats, and more from carbohydrate compared to adolescents who do not take vitamin and/or mineral supplements. Adolescents who take vitamin and/or mineral supplements also consume diets that tend to be more nutrient dense, higher in folate, calcium, iron, and vitamins E, C and A than adolescents who do not take vitamin and/or mineral supplements.

Physical Activity

Regular physical activity has many health benefits. Physical activity improves aerobic endurance, muscular strength and bone density. Regular physical activity can also help reduce the risk of overweight and obesity. Physical activity is related to higher levels of self-esteem and self-concept and lower levels of anxiety and stress among adolescents. Thus, regular physical activity is associated with both physiological and psychological benefits, especially during adolescence, which provides a positive influence for the adoption of lifelong physical activity.

Despite a common knowledge about the benefits and importance of regular physical activity, only about one-half of adolescents regularly participate in vigorous physical activity and one-fourth report no vigorous physical activity. In addition, regular physical activity steadily declines steadily during adolescence. Recommendations are that people of all ages include a minimum of 30 minutes of physical activity on most, if not all days of the week that require moderate to vigorous levels of exertion.

Many personal, social and environmental factors are associated with adolescent physical activity. Personal factors positively associated with being physically activity among adolescents include confidence in one's ability, having a positive attitude toward physical activity, enjoying physical activity, and perceiving positive benefits associated with physical activity. Social factors associated with participating in physical activity are peer and family support. Environmental factors associated with participation in physical activity are having safe and convenient places to play, sports equipment, and transportation to sports of fitness programs.

Schools offer an ideal setting for promoting regular physical activity through physical education classes. However, in recent years, participating in physical education classes in 9-12 grades has decreased significantly from approximately 40% to 25%. In addition, the number of students enrolled in physical education classes who report being physically active for at least 20 minutes in physical education class has declines. Communities providing access to being physically active are essential because most physical activity among adolescents occur outside of schools.

Overweight and Obesity

The incidence of overweight among adolescents over the past two decades has increased. Exact reasons for the increase in overweight have not been identified. Although genetics is known to contribute to the occurrence of overweight, and having one or more overweight parents increases the risk an adolescent developing obesity, genetics alone cannot account for the dramatic increase in overweight over the past two decades. Environmental factors, or interactions between genetic and environmental factors, are the most likely causes of the dramatic increase in overweight.

Risk factors for the development of overweight among children and adolescents include having at least one overweight parent; coming from a low income family; being of African American, Hispanic, or Native American descent; and being diagnosed with a physical condition that limits mobility. Inadequate levels of physical activity and consuming diets high in total calories and fat are additional risk factors for overweight for a significant proportion of adolescents. These environmental factors are believed to increase the risk of developing overweight if an adolescent is genetically predisposed to obesity.

Body mass index (BMI) is used to assess weight status among adolescents. BMI values are compared to appropriate age and gender percentiles. Adolescents with BMI's greater than the 85th but lower than the 95th percentile are considered at risk for overweight, those with BMI values above the 95th percentile are considered overweight. Growth curves based on BMI's for children and adolescents are available from the National Center for Health Statistics.

Being overweight can cause a number of medical, psychological and social complications among adolescents, including hypertension, elevated blood lipids, insulin resistance, type 2 diabetes, sleep apnea, orthopedic problems, body image disturbances and lowered self-esteem. The increase in type 2 diabetes among youth and adolescents is particularly alarming. One study reported that one-third of newly diagnosed diabetes where adolescents under the age of 20 and almost all of these were overweight.

Adolescents should have their weight-for-height screened on a yearly basis. Adolescents who are at-risk for overweight should have an in-depth medial assessment to diagnose any obesity-related complications. Weight maintenance is recommended for adolescents who are at-risk for overweight and have not yet completed puberty, unless medical complications are detected. Weight loss is recommended when medical complications are present in adolescents at-risk for overweight, when the adolescent is determined to be overweight, and among older adolescents who have completed physical growth and development.

Weight loss should not be attempted until the adolescent and his or her family demonstrates current weight can be maintained. For severely obese adolescents, as well as for those with significant medical complications, rapid weight loss may be required. No specific physical activities or dietary regimens are recommended for overweight adolescents. Reducing or eliminating the intake of "problem" foods such as savoury snacks or high-sugar beverages is often the first dietary change recommended.

Health care providers generally do not recommend calorie or fat gram counting for overweight adolescents. Replacing high-fat or high-sugar foods with healthier substitutes and regulating portion sizes has been shown to result in a better chance of long-term behaviour changes among adolescence. In addition, sedentary activities should be replaced with more strenuous activities.

Dieting Behaviours

Dieting behaviours among adolescents, in particular among adolescent females, is alarmingly high. One study reported that 50 to 60% of adolescent females consider they are overweight and have attempted to diet. Dieting behaviours among adolescents are of concern in that many adolescents who diet are not overweight. Many adolescents who diet adopt unhealthy dieting behaviours such as skipping meals, severely restricting calories or limited intake of foods from food groups. Dieting is associated with inadequate intakes of essential nutrients such as calcium. Dieting behaviours leading adolescents to experience hunger or cravings may place them at risk for binge eating episodes. Dieting at an early age may be indicative of increased risk for the later development of eating disorders. Therefore, dieting should not be viewed as a normal and acceptable behaviour, in particular among children and adolescents.

Body Dissatisfaction

During adolescence, body image and self-esteem tend to be closely related. Therefore, body image concerns should not be viewed as a normal and acceptable component of adolescence. Furthermore, body dissatisfaction is probably the main contributing factor to unhealthy dieting behaviours, disordered eating behaviours and clinical eating disorders. Body dissatisfaction is reported by a high percentage of adolescents. In a study, over 60% of adolescent females and about 35% of adolescent males were dissatisfied with their weight.

All adolescents, including overweight adolescents, should be encouraged to appreciate the positive aspects of their bodies. Overweight adolescents may need help in accepting the fact that they may never achieve the thin ideal portrayed in the media, but they may strive toward a leaner and healthier body that is realistic for them.

Eating Disorders

Serious eating disorders include anorexia nervosa, bulimia nervosa, and binge eating disorder. Many factors contribute to the etiology of eating disorders. Some of the major causative factors include social norms emphasizing thinness, being teased about one's weight, family relations, body shape and size, body image and self-esteem. These factors do not operate independently but interact with each other to increase the risk of an adolescent participating in potentially harmful eating and dieting behaviours. It is important to realize that different factors may lead to weight related disorders in different adolescents.

The complex etiology of eating disorders and the numerous potential psychological, social, physical and behavioural consequences indicate the need for a multidisciplinary treatment approach to eating disorders. The health care team caring for an adolescent with an eating disorder will often include a physician, dietitian, nurse, psychologist, and/or psychiatrist.

Importance of Nutrition in Aging

Aging is an inevitable and natural process. However, people can improve the quality of their life in later years, within limits, by adopting healthy lifestyle habits such as healthy eating and being physically active. Good nutrition and physical activity can help keep the body healthy, and may lower the risk of some conditions that can occur in later years.

Nutrient Needs of Older Adults

The Dietary Reference Intakes (DRI) provide dietary

recommendations for people over 50 years of age by two age groups, 51 to 70 years and 71 years and older.

The basic guidelines for a nutritious diet are about the same for most healthy older adults as most healthy younger adults. The Food Guide Pyramid is the best dietary tool to help older adults get the variety and amount of nutrients they need every day. However, older adults do need to pay special attention to the quality of foods they eat. There are some changes in nutrient needs with aging.

— *Calories*: Calorie needs decrease with age as physical activity, muscle mass and the body's metabolism slows down. Calorie needs tend to decrease about 5% per decade. As a result, the RDA for calories for adults decreases slightly after age 50. Careful meal planning is important for older adults in order to get all the nutrients they need in fewer calories.

  Consuming more calories than what the body needs can result in weight gain. Excess weight is linked to many health problems. These include high blood pressure, heart disease, stroke, diabetes and certain cancers. An easy method to use to estimate calorie needs for older adults is to multiply current weight in pounds by an activity factor. Multiply 10 calories per pound if sedentary or desiring weight loss. Multiply 12 – 13 calories per pound if moderately active.

  Multiply 15 calories per pound if active. Consuming less than 1200 calories is not recommended because it's difficult to get all the nutrients needed in less than 1200 calories. Limiting intake of fatty foods, sweets, high-calorie snacks and alcohol can lower calorie intake and help with weight control. These foods contain lots of calories but few nutrients. Eating them in place of more nutritious foods can lead to weight gain without meeting nutritional needs.

  Some older adults do not eat enough food, particularly foods that supply necessary nutrients. As a result they may not get enough calories and nutrients to maintain health and well-being.

— *Protein*: Adequate protein is especially important for older adults in order to maintain healthy cells, sustain the immune system to help the body fight infections, and prevent muscle wasting. Protein is also needed for wound healing and to make enzymes and hormones. As a result, protein needs may actually increase due to surgery, illness or disease.

The Dietary Reference Intake (DRI) for protein for adults 18 years of age and older is 0.8 g/kg body weight. However, some research indicates that older adults may need slightly more protein (1.0 to 1.25 vs. 0.8 g/kg body weight, respectively).

Protein needs can be met by following the Food Guide Pyramid recommendations of two to three meat and two to three dairy servings each day. Because calorie needs decrease, protein must be obtain from lower fat sources of high-quality protein such as lean meats, poultry, fish and eggs; nonfat and low-fat milk products; and legumes. Many older adults limit meat and dairy foods to lower fat for weight loss. However, lowering fat in the diet doesn't mean omitting meat and dairy products. These foods are part of a well balanced diet, and there are many low-fat choices available.

— *Fat*: Fat is the most concentrated source of food energy. Fat helps form cell membranes and carries the fat-soluble vitamins A, D, E, and K. Fat also provides the essential fatty acids the body cannot make.

Although fat is important in the diet, many adults eat more fat than they should. High fat diets are a risk factor for heart disease, cancer, and obesity. By increasing the risk of obesity, high fat diets may indirectly increase risk of diabetes and high blood pressure. Recommendations are to keep saturated fat in the diet below 10% of total calories and total fat at or below 30% of total calories. Fat intake can be lowered by choosing lean meats and low-fat dairy products, using low-fat preparation methods, and limiting the use of added or hidden sources of fat.

— *Carbohydrate:* Carbohydrate provides energy for body cells and the central nervous system. Adequate carbohydrate is needed to protect protein from being used for energy. Recommendations are that 50 to 60 percent of calories should come from carbohydrate rich foods. Most should come from complex carbohydrate foods: cereals, grains, legumes, vegetables and fruits. These foods not only provide carbohydrate but they also supply vitamins, minerals and fiber. Simple carbohydrates or sugar-rich foods should be limited. The Food Guide Pyramid recommends at least six bread, cereal, rice or pasta servings, and five fruit and vegetable servings each day.

Many people think carbohydrate rich foods are fattening. Actually the "fattening" part is usually added. For example, a medium baked potato has approximately 80 calories. Adding 1 tablespoon of margarine and 2 tablespoons of sour cream, adds approximately 150 calories for a grand total of 230 calories of which 65% are fat calories.

— *Fiber:* Most older adults do not consume adequate fiber. Fiber comes in two basic types, soluble fiber and insoluble fiber. Both types of fiber are important for good health. Dietary fiber is beneficial for many health conditions, such as constipation, diarrhea, diverticulitis, cardiovascular disease, colon cancer, and diabetes. However, one should remember that dietary fiber is only one factor involved in these conditions.

Foods are the best way to increase fiber intake. Food sources of fiber include fruits, vegetables, whole grain breads and cereals, dried peas and beans, nuts and seeds. Cooking, processing, and removing peels can lower the fiber in foods. The DRI for fiber for adults 51 years of age and older is 21 grams of fiber per day for females and 30 grams of fiber per day for males, based on 14 grams fiber per 1,000 calories each day. This amount of fiber can be provided without using fiber supplements by following the Food Guide Pyramid recommendations of six whole-grain bread and cereal servings and five fruit and vegetable servings each day.

It is important to increase fiber in the diet slowly. Increasing fiber too fast may cause bloating and gas. Since fiber absorbs water it also is important to drink plenty of fluids when increasing dietary fiber. Older adults should check with their physician before increasing dietary fiber. Fiber intake may need to be limited for older adults who have chewing, swallowing or other medical problems.

— *Vitamins and Minerals*: Vitamin and Mineral needs for older adults are about the same as for younger adults. However, some differences in nutrient needs do occur with age.

— *Vitamin A.* Vitamin A needs decrease with age. In addition vitamin A is more readily stored in older adults than younger adults. This makes over-dosing with vitamin A supplements more common among older adults. The DRI for adults 51 years of age and older is 900 micrograms for males and 700 micrograms for females. The Tolerable Upper Level of Intake (UL) for vitamin A is 3,000 micrograms (3 milligrams) per day. Beta-carotene is a plant precursor of vitamin A and will does not cause a problem with over-dosing. Leading food sources of vitamin A and beta-carotene are carrots, ready-to-eat cereals and milk.

— *Iron.* Iron needs for women decrease after menopause. Like vitamin A, iron is stored more readily in older adults than in younger adults. Excess iron can increase oxidative stress. The DRI for adults 51 years of age and older is 8 milligrams per day. The UL for iron is

45 milligrams per day. Leading food sources of iron are ready-to-eat cereals, yeast bread and beef.

— *Vitamin D.* Vitamin D is needed to absorb calcium. Vitamin D needs increase with age. The ability of the body to synthesize the vitamin D precursor in the skin decreases with age. Older adults also tend to have less sunlight exposure either due to limited time in the sun, being homebound or use of sun blocks. The DRI for vitamin D is 10 micrograms (400 International Units) for people aged 51 to 70; and 15 micrograms (600 International Units) for people older than 70 years. The UL for vitamin D is 50 micrograms (2,000 IU). Leading food sources of vitamin D are fortified cereals, milk, eggs, liver, salmon, tuna, catfish and herring.

— *Vitamin B12.* An estimated 15% of older adults are defficient in vitamin B12. People with atrophic gastritis are particularly vulnerable to vitamin B12 deficiency. B12 deficiency can result in irreversible nerve damage. Many older adults lose their ability to adequately absorb the naturally occurring form of B12 found in food. In order to absorb naturally occurring B12 from food the body must split it from a protein carrier. Older adults may absorb vitamin B12 better in synthetic form, which is not bound to a protein carrier, than from food. The DRI for vitamin B12 for adults 51 years of age is 2.4 micrograms per day. Synthetic vitamin B12 is found in fortified foods such as cereals. Protein-bound B12 is found in all animal products. Leading food sources of vitamin B12 are beef, milk, fish and shellfish.

— *Calcium.* Older adults should pay particular attention to their need for calcium as reflected by the higher calcium DRI for older adults. Many older adults do not consume enough calcium. An adequate calcium intake is one way to help protect against osteoporosis. Osteoporosis is a condition, which thins the bones and can lead to painful fractures. The DRI for calcium for adults 51 years of age and older is 1200 milligrams per day. The UL for calcium is 2,500 milligrams per day. Leading food sources of calcium are milk, yogurt, cheese and other dairy products, dark green leafy vegetables, such as broccoli and canned salmon.

In addition to some changes in vitamin and mineral requirements with age, older adults tend to have low dietary intakes of some vitamins and minerals.

— *Vitamin E.* Vitamin E is an antioxidant. Vitamin E plays an important role in the health of older adult due to its antioxidant functions, such as decreasing the development of cataracts and heart disease. Vitamin E is also associated with increased immune function. The DRI for vitamin E for adults age 51 years of age and older is 15 milligrams or 15 IU alpha-tocopherol equivalents (TE). The UL for vitamin E is 1,000 mg or IU. Leading food sources of vitamin E are salad dressings/mayonnaise, margarine, and ready-to-eat cereals. Other good sources of vitamin E are oils, especially sunflower and safflower oils, fats, whole grains, wheat germ, leafy green vegetables, tomatoes, nuts, seeds and eggs.

— *Folate.* Adequate folate can decrease blood homocysteine levels, which are a risk factor for heart disease. The DRI for folate for male and females, 51 years of age and older is 400 micrograms per day. The UL for folate is 1,000 micrograms from supplements and fortified foods. Leading food sources of folate are ready-to-eat cereals, yeast bread, orange juice and grapefruit juice.

— *Magnesium.* Adequate magnesium is needed for bone and tooth formation, nerve activity, and metabolism of carbohydrates, protein and fat. The DRI for magnesium for adults 51 years of age and older is 420 milligrams for males and 320 milligrams for females per day. The UL for magnesium is 350 milligrams from supplements and medications. Leading food sources of magnesium are milk, yeast bread, coffee, ready-to-eat cereal, beef and potatoes.

— *Zinc*. Zinc deficiency is related to delayed wound healing, decreased taste acuity and immune response, and increases risk of dermatitis. The DRI for zinc for adults 51 years of age and older is 8 milligrams for females and 11 milligrams for males per day. The UL for zinc is 40 milligrams per day. Leading food sources of zinc are beef, ready-to-eat cereals, milk and poultry.

— *Water*: Water is more critical to life than food. Lack of water can result in death sooner than will lack of food. Older adults need at least six to eight cups of water each day. An easy guide to water intake is 1 milliliter of fluid per calorie eaten, with a minimum of 1500 milliliters (6 cups). Thus for a 2,000 calorie diet, this would be 2,000 milliliters fluid or 8 cups.

Water can be taken in many forms such as water, fruit juice, milk, soups, coffee, tea or soft drinks. Because caffeine can cause water loss, decaffeinated fluids are recommended instead of caffeinated fluids.

However, despite fluids being available, many older adults become dehydrated. Dehydrated older adults are more susceptible to urinary tract infections, pneumonia, pressure ulcers, confusion and disorientation. Older adults are at higher risk for dehydration. Body water decreases with age, leaving a smaller margin of safety for older adults. Many medications older adults use also increase in water loss. In addition, the thirst mechanism is not as effective in older adults. As a result, older adults do not seem to notice thirst and consume water in response.

Fear of incontinence and increased arthritic pain resulting from numerous trips to the toilet may also interfere with consumption of adequate fluid intake. As a result, many older adults limit their fluid intake. Decreased mobility may also limit fluid intake. If an older adult is bed-ridden or wheelchair bound it may be difficult for them to reach fluids. Keep fluids close at hand in a pitcher or glass to encourage increase fluid intake. If a person is very weak or frail using a small glass, or using a straw may make fluid intake easier. The following table shows some common signs of dehydration.

Percent Loss of Body Water	Common Signs of Dehydration
0-1%	Thirst
2-5%	Dry mouth, flushed skin, fatigue, headache, impaired physical performance
6%	Increased body temperature, breathing rate, and pulse rate
8%	Dizziness, increased weakness, labored breathing with exercise
10%	Muscle spasms, swollen tongue, delirium
11%	Poor blood circulation, failing kidney function

— *Vitamin and Mineral Supplements*: Many older adults can get the nutrients they need by eating a wide variety of nutritious foods each day following the Food Guide Pyramid. The greater the variety the less likely one is to develop either a deficiency or an excess of any single nutrient and the more likely one is to stay healthy. There are a large number of nutrients that are essential to health, but vitamin and mineral supplements only contain some of them. A well-balanced diet one that contains a variety of foods will provide all the necessary nutrients. Foods may also contain some essential nutrients that have not yet been identified.

However, some older adults do not always get all the vitamins and minerals they need from their daily diet. Digestive problems, chewing difficulties, and the use of certain drugs can all interfere with good nutrition. Therefore, while it is possible for older adults to get all the nutrients for good health from food, they many not do so. Older adults with these problems may benefit from a multivitamin and/or multi-mineral supplement.

However, older adults should not take isolated vitamin and/or mineral supplements unless recommended by a physician. In addition, older adults should not take large doses (amounts far greater than the Dietary Reference Intakes) without specific medical recommendations. One might think that more is better when taking vitamin or mineral supplements. However, a vitamin or mineral taken in large amounts can be dangerous. Overdoses happen easier with supplements than with food. Minerals and in large amounts can be dangerous as can vitamins. Our bodies store excess minerals and fat-soluble vitamins (vitamins A, D, E, and K). Excessive amounts of these nutrients can accumulate and be harmful.

Dangerous levels can produce such symptoms as nausea, vomiting, and other serious side effects. Toxicity from water-soluble vitamins, such as vitamin C, is unlikely since excess amounts are flushed from the body in the urine. However, serious side effects can occur even with water-soluble vitamins. Because nutrients interact with each other, a balance of all nutrients is important. If the body has too much or too little of any nutrient it can affect how the body uses other nutrients.

Vitamin or mineral supplements cannot make up for a poor diet. No supplement contains all the essential nutrients the body needs. The basis for good health depends on a well balanced diet from a variety of foods. The keys to good nutrition are variety and moderation. The greater the variety of foods, the less likely a deficiency or excess of any one vitamin or mineral will occur. Following the Food Guide Pyramid is the best guide for getting the right foods in the right amounts for good health.

Medications May Affect Nutrient Needs

Older adults should follow their doctor's advice about eating, especially if they have an illness that requires changes in what or how they eat, or if they are taking medications. Some drugs interact with certain foods, or can affect appetite. In addition, some foods can interact with medications.

Physical Changes That May Affect Food Intake

Physical changes with aging can affect food intake. These changes usually occur at a different rates from person to person. Some physical functions change little with aging while others greatly change. The following are some physical changes that may affect dietary intake.

— *Body Composition*: Many adults lose muscle, bone mineral and body water with aging. At the same time, many older adults gain body fat. Muscle loss can cause people to lose their ability to move and maintain balance, making falls likely. A loss of muscle is not inevitable. Good nutrition and regular physical activity can help maintain muscle mass and strength. Strength training can increase muscle and decrease body fat. Weight bearing and resistance activities also increase muscle and bone density. Since muscle contains more water than fat, building muscle also helps increase body water.

— *Weight Gain*: Although not inevitable, weight gain is common with aging due to a shift in body composition, decrease in metabolism and decrease in physical activity.

— *Saliva*: Production of saliva may decrease with age. Saliva moistens food and makes swallowing easier. Foods may be dry and more difficult to swallow.

— *Teeth*: Loss of teeth makes eating and chewing some foods difficult. Many older adults are unable to adjust to dentures or have dentures that do not fit. People with tooth loss, gum disease, or poor fitting dentures tend to eat softer foods or limiting food intake can lead to a poor diet. Poor chewing can also increase the risk of choking.

— *Stomach Acid*: Production and secretion of stomach acid tends to decrease with age. This causes decreased digestion and a feeling of indigestion.

— *Digestion*: Many older adults find that they do not digest foods as well as when they were younger. Intestinal secretions tend to change with aging. Atrophic gastritis, a condition that affects almost a third of those over 60, is characterized by an inflamed stomach, bacterial overgrowth, and a lack of hydrochloric acid and intrinsic factor – all of which can impair the digestion and absorption of nutrients, most notably vitamin B12, but also biotin, folate, calcium, iron and zinc. Serving four to six smaller meals may be more acceptable. Allow plenty of time, don't rush meals, and have a pleasant environment. Many older adults do not tolerance of high fat or dairy foods.

— *Fat Tolerance*: Many adults find that they do not tolerate high fatty foods as well with age. Decrease the amount of fat added to foods, choose low-fat foods and use low-fat preparation methods to decrease fat intake. This will also help control calories.

— *Lactose Intolerance*: Many adults do not tolerate milk and milk products as well with age. However, some find that they can tolerate small amounts of milk, or fermented milk products such as buttermilk, yogurt and cheese. It is important to maintain calcium intake through foods rich in calcium to reduce the risk of osteoporosis. Lactaid or Dairy Ease can be used to help with the digestion of milk or milk products.

— *Constipation*: Constipation is a common problem among older adults. The intestinal wall tends to lose strength and elasticity with age which results in slower intestinal motility. Sufficient fiber and fluids are important to combat constipation. Increase intake of raw and/or cooked fruits and vegetables, and whole grain breads and cereals to increase fiber intake. Fiber supplements are not necessary with adequate dietary fiber intake. Exercise is also important in reducing constipation. Do not use mineral oils. These can cause loss of fat-soluble vitamins.

— *Thirst*: Older adults thirst mechanism is not as effective as that of younger adults. As a result, older adults do not notice thirst, and consume water in response to need, as well as younger adults. The combined effects of decreased thirst sensation, decreased body water, increased water loss, incontinence and decreased mobility put older adults at greater risk for dehydration.

— *Taste and Smell*: Taste and smell tend to decline with age. This is because the number of taste buds and olfactory cells, the functional unit in smelling, decrease with age. Medicines also can interfere with the taste of foods. Changes in taste and smell may decrease one's appetite for foods resulting in a poor diet.

— *Eyesight*: Eyesight tends to decline with age. This can make shopping, cooking, and possibly eating become more difficult. Problems reading small print recipes or seeing oven temperatures may result in less meal preparation.

— *Strength and Energy*: Strength and energy often decline with increasing age. Food shopping, carrying heavy groceries, choosing from a wide variety of foods and preparing meals may become difficult. Keeping a reserve supply of food on hand for sick days or when the weather is bad is helpful.

The following are some foods to keep on hand.

— Meats and Meat Alternatives: tuna in water, canned meats, dried beans

— Fruits: canned fruits, dried fruits

— Vegetables: canned vegetables, frozen vegetables

— Dairy Foods: nonfat dried milk

— Bread and Cereals: ready to eat cereals, hot cooked cereals, crackers, rice, pasta

— Convenience Foods: macaroni and cheese mixes, low-sodium canned soups, pudding mixes, dry soup mixes, peanut butter, jelly.

Psychological, Social and Economic Changes

— *Psychological Changes*: Although not inevitable, depression is common among older adults. Depression can cause loss of appetite and decreased motivation to cook or even eat. Overwhelming grief at the death of a spouse, friend, or family member can leave a person, especially an older person feeling powerless to overcome depression. When a person is suffering from depression, cooking meals may not seem worthwhile.

— *Social Changes*: Loneliness is a major problem for many older adults who live and eat alone. When one is lonely there is little motivation to prepare and eat a well-balanced meal. Loneliness can decrease ones' appetite and lead to monotonous meals, snacking, and eating easily prepared, cheaper and softer foods. Such dietary habits can eventually lead to a poor diet. Senior citizen nutrition programs, churches and other community groups offer nutritious meals, fellowship and transportation that can help with food intake.

— *Economic Changes*: Many older adults have limited incomes, which may result in less money for food. Some older adults have to move into less expensive living areas which may have poor facilities for storing and preparing foods. There may be little money for transportation to grocery stores. These limitations can dramatically decrease the quality of ones' diet and affect ones' attitude towards eating.

Tips To Maintain A Healthy Diet

— Include foods from the Food Guide Pyramid food groups first. Avoid empty calorie foods such as desserts, sweets and fats that provide few nutrients for the calories.

— Use fresh fruits for dessert.

— If food intake is low encourage in between meal snacks. Try fruits, crackers and cheese or peanut butter.

— Drink at least 6 to 8 glasses of fluid each day to prevent constipation and dehydration. Adequate fiber from whole grain breads and cereals, fruits and vegetables, and exercise can also help with constipation.

— Eat slowly and chew thoroughly.

— Include a variety of foods and spices, unless specific foods and spices are not well tolerated.

— If milk causes intestinal distress, try fermented cheeses, yogurt, or smaller servings. Lactaid or Dairy Ease can be used to help with the digestion of milk or milk products.

Tips if Appetite Decreases

— Eat meals at regular times.

— Have the big meal of the day at breakfast or lunch when appetite is larger and keep dinner small.

— Plan 5 or 6 smaller meals.

— Walk daily to increase activity and appetite.

Tips if Taste and Smell Decreases

— Use herbs and spices, unless they are not tolerated. Taste decreases with age and using herbs, spices and lemon juice can increase the flavour of foods. Try growing you own herbs, either in a garden or in a pot on a sunny windowsill.

— Flavors are more pronounced if food is served at body temperature. Flavors are not as easy to detect in cold and hot foods.

Tips if Chewing and Swallowing Decrease Food Intake

— Use gravy or sauces if swallowing is a problem.

— Serve a beverage with the meal to help with swallowing.

— Eat slowly and chew food thoroughly.

— Be sure dentures fit properly.

— Try to maintain a normal diet, and avoid using baby foods or ground foods if possible. Ground food becomes dry and difficult to swallow. Using baby foods makes an individual feel like they are not in control of their food intake.

— Use soft high protein foods to maintain protein intake if the individual is not able to chew regular meats. Try moist meat loaf, deviled eggs, egg salad, soft meat salads, soups, puddings and custards. These softer meats or meat alternatives are easier to chew and swallow.

— Try precutting foods and putting the smaller bite size pieces into casseroles, soups or gelatin. Foods prepared this way are easier to eat but the individual still feels like they are eating regular foods. Try mashing if that is an acceptable food form such as mashed potatoes or mashed baked squash. Try shredding raw vegetables or fruits and using the shredded vegetables and fruits in salads, gelatins or stir-fry.

Tips if Emotional and Social Factors Decrease Food Intake

— Serve food attractively. Food tastes better if it looks good to eat. Try colourful placemats or trays, or a centerpiece to improve the appearance.

— Serve foods with a variety of flavors, colours, temperatures and textures. Meals with a variety of food flavors, colours, temperatures and textures are more appealing.

— Don't serve the same foods day after day.

— Make the surroundings pleasant. Try setting up the food tray next to a window with a view.

— Try turning on the television or radio if the individual has to eat alone.

— Invite friends or relatives over to share a meal from time to time.

— Eat out occasionally. Go to a meal at a senior citizens center or a restaurant that features senior citizen discounts.

4

Effect of Heredity and Environment

In many competitive sports, the difference between the gold medal and also-ran status is a fraction of a second. No wonder everyone is looking for any edge that technology might offer. Athletic improvements over the past decade have come to depend more and more on scientific advances in training, nutrition, and even surgical enhancements. But perhaps the biggest boost has come from performance-enhancing additives. With the widespread use of steroids, human growth hormone and EPO (Erythropoietin, a hormone that regulates red blood cell production, used to increase the oxygen-carrying capacity, and hence the performance, of endurance athletes), runners, bikers, or swimmers leaning into the wind and water have every reason to eye their competitors suspiciously.

Now the cornucopia of easily available and easily disguisable pharmaceuticals is joined by the latest and most controversial competitive weapon - genetic engineering. Several promising performance-enhancing gene modifications have already been successfully tested on animals. They include generating the growth of explosive, fast-twitch muscle fibres and stimulating the release of growth-hormone-releasing hormone (GHRH), which can make recipients both stronger and leaner. Medical applications of gene therapy on humans to cure or prevent disease are at a rudimentary but fast-evolving stage.

Instead of treating deficiencies by injecting drugs, doctors soon will be able to prescribe genetic treatments that will induce the body's own machinery to produce the proteins needed to combat illnesses. 'It's not rocket science,' says Theodore Fridemann, director of the gene therapy programme at the University of California at San Diego and a member of the medical research committee of the World Anti-Doping Agency (WADA). 'If you asked any student of molecular biology how he would implant genes to change muscle function, he could cite three or four ways to do it.'

The model cited by scientists on the cutting edge of sports science - the experimental patient that sends shivers down the back of the Greenes, the Kipketers, and the Khannouchis of this world - is 'He-Man', a mouse running endless, tireless circles in his basement laboratory cage at a University of Pennsylvania physiology laboratory. Two years ago, He-Man was injected with a synthetic version of a gene called Insulin-like Growth Factor 1 (IGF-1), a protein that makes muscles grow and repair themselves. Today, deep into old age, the once tiny mouse and his gene-modified brothers and sisters look more like the Turkish weight-lifting icon Naim Suleymanoglu. After the IGF-1 boosted He-Man's muscle mass by more than 60%, he can now climb a ladder carrying three times his body weight.

As the drug-addled East German and Soviet sports systems demonstrated, athletes and their managers are willing to strike Faustian bargains to achieve immediate glory. But this was no Communist-specific phenomenon: in a 1995 survey of nearly 200 aspiring American Olympians, more than half said they would take a banned substance that would guarantee victory in every competition for five years even if it would lead to certain death. Like ordinary genes, the artificial genes consist of DNA, the basic raw materials of human life. The direct delivery approach would be to inject the DNA into the muscle.

The fibres would then take up the DNA and add it to the normal pool of genes. As this method is not yet very efficient, researchers often use viruses to carry the gene payload into a cell's nuclei. That's how the IGF-1 gene was delivered to make He-Man. Unfortunately, in contrast to the direct injection, the genes are also delivered to many other cells, such as those of the blood and liver, in addition to the intended target. A third approach entails removing specific cell types from the patient, adding the artificial gene in the laboratory and reintroducing the cells into the body. Since the artificial genes would produce proteins that in many cases are identical to the normal proteins, that means you can kiss good-bye to effective policing by sports agencies.

Bengt Saltin has a recurring nightmare. He imagines a scenario in which an already elite sprinter obsessed with becoming the world's fastest human turns to a renegade geneticist familiar with the latest research on the genetic modification of muscle fibre types. As powerful as the human musculature may appear to be to the layman, it can't hold a candle, relatively, to the explosive capacity of the muscles of many mammals, including mice, who call on energy bursts to elude predators. Although the fastest muscle fibre types are not found in human skeletal muscle, the potential for developing such fibres are imbedded in long dormant genes. Geneticists have recently developed a protein known as a 'transcription factor' called Velociphin, which can activate these genes.

Just a few injections of this DNA into the quadriceps, hamstring, and gluteus, and the muscle fibres will start cranking out Velociphin, which will activate the fast myosin gene. In weeks, the muscles bulge and burst with energy. There are no visible side-effects and without a muscle biopsy directly into manipulated muscle, the genetic modification is undetectable. It's the long-awaited race for Olympic immortality. BANG! The genetically doped athlete dashes into the lead, extending it with every stride. Then at 65 metres, far out in front of the field, a sudden twinge tickles the hamstring. Saltin picks up the story. At 80m, the twinge explodes into an overwhelming pain as he pulls his hamstring. A tenth of a second later the patella tendon gives in, because it is no match for the massive forces generated by his quadriceps muscle.

The patella tendon pulls out part of the tibia bone, which then snaps, and the entire quadriceps shoots up along the femur bone. The athlete crumples to the ground, his running career over. 'This is not the scenario that generally comes to mind in connection with the words 'genetically engineered super athlete',' notes Saltin, but it is part of the reality. For example, researchers have genetically altered a housefly with muscles 300% stronger than normal.

It may sound promising, but 'the fly actually lost power because it couldn't make its wings move fast enough' to support the added muscle weight, notes H. Lee Sweeney, co-author of the He-Man study. While society has come to view the human body as an invincible machine, it is in fact a resilient but still delicate balance of tendons, cartilage, muscle, and fat. This is a balance that some fear may be altered radically, permanently, and perhaps perilously by genetic manipulation.

Ethical Concerns and Practical Problems

This has understandably provoked a host of medical and ethical concerns. 'The only thing keeping athletes from using genetic manipulation today is the control problem,' says Saltin. 'You can't shut the production off when you want to.' For example, muscles injected with Velociphin will continue to produce the explosive fibres without further injection. Geneticists experimenting with the gene that codes for EPO have discovered that a single injection into the leg muscles of monkeys produced significantly elevated red blood cell levels for 20 to 30 weeks.

That could prove to be a boon for anemia patients and provide a performance boost for endurance athletes except for one key problem: in the absence of a mechanism to shut down production, the body could turn into a out-of-control EPO factory, leading to the thickening of the blood with excessive blood cells, strokes, heart attacks, and eventually death. But such problems offer only temporary barriers. Helen Blau, chairwoman of the department of molecular pharmacology at Stanford Medical School, has demonstrated that a gene could be introduced into a mouse to stimulate growth hormone in the bloodstream and then be switched off with the use of an oral antibiotic.

'In theory, it is possible that an athlete could be genetically engineered to have a gene so you could increase muscle strength, train with it and shut it off when you want to,' she says. Not only would such a development prevent inserted genes from spinning out of control, they would render drug screening almost impossible. With all of these Frankenstein-like scenarios, it would seem an easy decision to ban genetic engineering of athletes on ethical grounds. 'The argument in favour of allowing people to do this is based on our tradition of giving individuals a huge amount of autonomy over their own bodies,' says Eric Juengst, an ethicist at Case Western Reserve University in Cleveland. 'The limits on that kind of freedom are interpersonal. Once your actions cross the line of affecting just yourself and begin to affect other people, we have licence to step in.'

Surprisingly, not everyone agrees, and in fact the ethical issues turn very murky on close examination. The current anti-doping rules do not permit the use of steroids even if prescribed for genuine medical reasons, eg to hasten recovery after an injury. Yet that is exactly how gene modification in athletes will first be used - say an injection of IGF-1 to stimulate muscle regeneration. Its use could theoretically allow an athlete to perform at an optimal level years past what is now considered his prime. Or imagine an athlete using gene modification to help overcome congenital asthma or some other genetic abnormality.

IOC President Jacques Rogge waded into this ethical thicket earlier this year. 'Genetic manipulation is there to treat people who have ailments, not there to treat a healthy person,' he says. 'I am very clear on this.' Very few geneticists or ethicists have quite the same level of clarity. There is a very hazy and debatable line separating 'health restoration' and 'performance enhancement'. The case of Helen Smith, an internationally renowned swimming star from Britain comes to mind. Smith who competes as a quadriplegic was threatened with a ban at the 2000 Sydney Paralympics for receiving medication that is life-sustaining for her but was deemed performance-enhancing by Olympic officials.

There is already an equal access controversy in elite sports between wealthier countries which employ cutting edge technology in equipment, nutrition, and medicines versus the rest of the world who just muddle along. What makes genetic engineering any different as long as its focus is in overcoming some real - or perceived - injury-related performance deficiency? A further question arises about any kind of genetic manipulation that is introduced before birth by a well-meaning parent. As Maurice Greene has noted: 'What if you're born with something having been done to you?' Would manipulation of an egg or an embryo be considered cheating, if as Greene hypothesises, 'you don't have anything to do with it?' It might be unfair to penalise someone for an enhanced genotype but it is understandably problematic to have that person compete against a non-enhanced athlete.

Considering the health dimension of genetic enhancement, it certainly appears to be a more acceptable method of performance enhancement than drugs. The IOC has set up a 'gene doping' advisory group but seems befuddled by these complex issues. 'The information from genetic science will feed through into better treatments for disease, but it also going to present the sports industry with a Pandora's box within the next five to 10 years,' says Bruce Lynn, a senior neurophysiologist at University College London's School of Human Health and Performance. There has even been talk of introducing a handicap for genetically enhanced contestants or even setting up official performance-enhanced competitions. 'That's a terrible idea,' bemoans Saltin. 'If genetic engineering is sanctioned, it's the end of sports as we know it. Sports will be a circus of unbelievable performances.'

From a purely competitive standpoint, athletics might be more exciting, pushing the edge of human capability, testing the limits of speed and endurance well beyond those that science currently accepts. Until the patella tendon and quadriceps snap and a once valiant athlete is carted off the track, perhaps never to walk again. Exercise Equipment: How sweat sweeps away gym germs. If you're like most people who work out in the gym, you don't particularly enjoy finding the weight bench you are about to use bathed in sweat from the previous occupant; nor do you like picking up dumbbells with wet grips - or sitting down on humid exercise bike seats. What could be more unpleasant? After all, you reason, isn't the sweat on your favourite leg-extension machine - being nothing less than a random sample of someone else's body fluids - simply a repository for whatever pathogens that individual might be harbouring in his/her body?

Concerns about sweaty equipment stimulate many gym athletes to set up their own fitness centres at home. Others take care never to be without a towel when working out at the gym. But does towelling off a hamstring-curl device really remove the germs along with the fluid? Carrying a spray can of disinfectant around the gym is definitely not cool, so what is the gym athlete - surrounded by a sea of apparently unfriendly sweat - supposed to do? Can you sit on someone else's sweat without worry? According to Birgit Schittek of the Department of Dermatology at Eberhard-Karls University in Tubingen, Germany, you shouldn't sweat it! She and her colleagues have discovered a substance in human sweat that kills many types of common bacteria and yeasts. The compound is so potent that sweat may reasonably be viewed as an anti-infection agent, rather than a fluid festering with disease.

A substance in human sweat kills many types of common bacteria and yeasts. Schittek discovered sweat's key pathogen-fighting chemical - dermcidin - almost by accident. In her primary work with genes involved in the development of the skin cancer malignant melanoma and a related benign condition, she and her co-workers found a unique strip of genetic material with an unknown function. The gene, called DCD, was not active in a variety of human tissues, including the nervous system, digestive organs and blood, but it was expressed strongly in human skin.

More specifically, the gene appeared to be most active in cells making up human sweat glands, which are located in the dermis - the thick layer of living tissue that lies beneath the outer layer, or epidermis. After a bit of scientific sleuthing, Schittek worked out that DCD coded for a protein called dermcidin. She was initially unsure of dermcidin's function, but guessed - quite reasonably - that it might have some anti-microbial properties. After all, human skin contains a number of defences against microbes. The skin itself, containing layers of cells stacked up on each other, represents a physical barrier against would-be invading pathogens.

In addition, human skin contains two types of anti-microbial proteins, the 'cathelicidins' and the 'defensins'. Cathelicidins, which appear to kill bacteria via a unique electrical-charge effect, are produced by skin cells called keratinocyctes and are frequently found in skin wounds and sites of skin inflammation. There are a variety of different defensins, which are produced by skin cells as well as white blood cells; some defensins work against 'gram-negative', potentially disease-causing bacteria like E coli, while others go to war with nasty 'gram-positive' bacteria, such as Staphylococcus aureus, a major cause of skin infections. To see what dermcidin could do, Schittek mixed it - in concentrations typically observed in sweat - with unpleasant skin pathogens such as E coli, S aureus, Enterococcus faecalis (the name suggests its favourite habitat) and also Candida albicans, which is a yeast rather than a bacterium.

During four hours of incubation in a basic sodium-phosphate buffer solution with a pH of 7.4 - the same acid-base balance as the blood - dermcidin killed 100% of the bacteria and was also a potent destroyer of C albicans! Of course, sweat is actually more acidic than blood, with a pH which can range from 4 to 6.8; sweat also contains varying concentrations of sodium (20-60 mM), chloride (20-80 mM), potassium (10 mM), and magnesium (1 mM). To see if dermcidin was active in sweat, Schittek tested the chemical's activity at a pH of 5.5 over a range of sodium concentrations and found that it remained a tough combatant against germs. 'It's very efficient - a very low concentration kills these four (common) microorganisms,' says Schittek. 'It's the first peptide which is constantly produced by the skin. The other antimicrobial peptides, the defensins, are also produced by skin cells, but only after inflammation.

From one perspective, sweating is the first line of defence against infection Schittek is not yet sure how dermcidin actually works. Many anti-microbial proteins possess a positive charge and kill bacteria by disrupting their membranes electrically, but dermcidin's charge is negative. It's also not clear whether dermcidin production increases during heavy sweating (are wetter gym seats safer?) - or if dermcidin synthesis varies significantly between people. One guess is that individuals who are prone to skin infections have naturally low levels of the key defence chemical.

Researchers believe that dermcidin may be effective against bacteria which have become resistant to conventional antibiotics, and they are also intrigued by the possibility that dermcidin might work in other parts of the body as well as the skin. Eventually we may see dermcidin marketed - in ointment or liquid form - as a topical skin application, a somewhat comforting thought the next time you find sweat (and its accompanying dermcidin) applied copiously to your favourite gym appliance. From one perspective, sweating is the first line of defence against infectious agents, so the 'rude' person who left sweat for you may have actually just been cleaning off the equipment!

Genetics and Performance

Scientists are slowly beginning to find the genes which play a direct role in determining exercise capacity. Recently, researchers discovered - on human chromosome No. 1 - the gene which encodes MCT1, a protein which helps transport lactate into muscle cells. Variations in this gene will no doubt determine how well an athlete can improve lactate threshold - a key predictor of endurance performance - in response to strenuous physical training. Now, scientists at the Royal Defence Medical College and the Centre for Cardiovascular Genetics in the UK have discovered that variations in the gene which encodes a protein called angiotensin-converting enzyme (ACE) can have a large impact on exercise efficiency.

To understand how variations in the ACE gene might influence the economy with which you run, cycle, or swim, you first need to understand what angiotensin-converting enzyme actually does. The angiotensin-converting-enzyme story begins with a plasma protein called angiotensinogen, which is present in the blood of all human beings. Under certain conditions, kidney cells secrete a hormone called renin into the blood which cleaves a 10-amino-acid protein from angiotensinogen to form a compound called angiotensin I. The various physiological roles played by angiotensin I are not completely understood, but it is known that angiotensin-converting enzyme (ACE) can knock two amino acids off angiotensin I to form a compound called angiotensin II.

Angiotensin II has a variety of functions, but for purposes of the discussion we can simply say that it directly increases blood pressure by constricting arteries, and it indirectly raises blood pressure and blood volume by stimulating thirst centres in the brain and directing the kidneys to conserve more minerals and water. The British scientists knew that there were two key variations in the ACE gene (the one which codes for angiotensin-converting enzyme). One of these has an extra 287 base pairs within its DNA and is called the 'long allele'; the other is without the base pairs and is the 'short allele'. All humans have two ACE genes; roughly 50 per cent of the world's population has one copy of each variant, 25 per cent have two short genes, and 25 per cent have the two long ones.

Previous studies had shown that the long allele seems to be linked with better endurance performance and a stronger response to exercise training. For example, in one piece of research individuals with two copies of the long allele gained more muscle mass and lost more body fat during 10 weeks of intensive physical training, compared with athletes with two copies of the short gene or one copy of each gene. The British researchers were not sure why that was the case, but they did know that the long allele produces a version of angiotensin-converting enzyme which is 'weaker', i. e., has lower activity, compared with the short gene. To gain a better understanding of the long-gene's effects, they recruited 58 Caucasian military servicemen into their study; 35 had two copies of the long version of the gene, and 23 possessed just the short version. All 58 men underwent an 11-week programme of endurance exercise consisting of interval training on an exercise bike.

Delta Efficiency

Prior to and after the training period, the researchers calculated the 'delta efficiency' of exercise for each subject. This variable is supposed to represent the efficiency with which muscles are working, and it is basically the percentage ratio of the change in work performed per minute to the change in energy expended per minute. Delta efficiency is not a bad way to measure one's economy of exercise; basically, it reflects the fact that if you can increase your rate of working per minute (i. e., your muscular power output) without a large upswing in energy expenditure, you are efficient; if your energy consumption soars when you increase your running, cycling, or swimming speed, you are inefficient. Before the training began, the delta efficiency was the same for both groups of men (about 25 per cent).

However, after training delta efficiency improved by almost 9 per cent for exercisers with two copies of the long ACE gene but remained stagnant in the short-ACE group.

What was going on? Bear in mind that one of the key - but often overlooked - adaptations you make to exercise training is in the responsiveness of your blood vessels. After you have been exercising regularly for a couple of months, your blood vessels relax more easily during exercise, increasing blood flow to your muscles. This has some obvious advantages; the spiked blood flow can bring more oxygen and fuel to your muscle fibres. At least some of this artery expansiveness is mediated by a chemical called nitric oxide which is released by cells lining your arteries (these cells help make up the 'endothelium' - the inner layer of artery walls).

Nitric oxide - 'discovered' by scientists about 20 years ago and originally thought to be an intracellular 'messenger' - not only dilates arteries but also prolongs vasodilation, keeping the good stuff flowing into your muscle cells throughout your workout or race. Incidentally, nitric oxide's actions are so powerful that nitric-oxide treatments reduce pulmonary vascular resistance in people with severe chronic obstructive pulmonary disease and are also thought to be helpful in the treatment of atherosclerosis.

Exercise training increases the production of nitric oxide by your endothelium, but angiotensin II seems to decrease the rate at which nitric oxide is synthesized. Thus, we have a potential mechanism underlying the long-ACE-gene's link with better endurance performance. The long gene produces angiotensin-converting enzyme with lower activity, which means that less angiotensin II will be produced. The lower angiotensin II means that more nitric oxide can be synthesized inside artery walls during exercise, leading to stronger blood flow to the muscles. In effect, the long ACE genes let endurance-trained muscles have more blood. It's not clear yet why this effect would improve efficiency of exercise (it seems more likely to raise VO2max and lactate threshold), unless the muscle cells most responsible for efficient movement are better supplied by oxygen and fuel in individuals with the longer ACE gene - and thus can work more continuously throughout a bout of exercise.

The exercise intensities utilized in the study were low (no higher than 80 Watts), so it's possible that the combination of long ACE genes plus training opened up blood flow to slow-twitch muscle cells in the exercisers' legs, allowing them to 'take over' the burden of exercise (slow-twitch cells would be more efficient than fast twitchers at low intensities of exertion). However, Dr. Hugh Montgomery, lead scientist in the study, believes that another mechanism may be at work. Montgomery thinks that the long ACE genes may have profound metabolic effects within the muscle cells, in addition to their influence on artery walls. Basically, he suggests that the long genes may improve the efficiency of fuel selection, uptake, and utilization by muscle fibres during exercise, thus enhancing economy.

ACE of hearts

Before rushing out to your local exercise geneticist to find out if you have the long version of ACE, bear in mind this caveat, however: so far, the efficiency improvement has only been detected at very low exercise intensities. Of course, many will wonder whether Kenyan runners have the long-ACE genes (but probably won't speculate on how the Ethiopians were able to borrow those ACEs from the Kenyans, or how the Kenyans picked up the genes from the Finns, who borrowed them from the Brits, who took the alleles from earlier Finns, who got them from Swedes, etc.).

Before this kind of thinking goes too far, however, we should point out that about 25 per cent of British and American citizens have double-long ACE genes, which in the case of Americans would mean that almost three times as many Americans hold double ACEs, compared to Kenyans, even if the entire Kenyan population had only the extended genes! It is clear that the research has implications which range beyond endurance exercise. Drugs called 'ACE inhibitors' help cardiac cells survive heart attacks and also improve survivorship in patients with heart troubles of various kinds by easing artery tightening and perhaps in part by letting nitric oxide do its thing and improving the efficiency of cardiac muscle-cell contractions. ACE inhibitors might also help increase the mechanical and metabolic efficiency of muscles in individuals who for various reasons are energy-deprived. The ACE work is exciting stuff, uncovering not only the genetic but also the important physiological foundations of exercise excellence.

African runners are genetically superior to white runners. Compared to whites, blacks are better suited for sports which involve short, explosive bursts of energy. Individuals from West Africa 'make' good sprinters, while people from East Africa are endurance types..Those are strong statements. Many people believe them. And implicit in the statements are two inferences that usually remain unstated:

1. If blacks are physically exceptional, then they don't have to go through the mental turmoil of constructing a rigorous training programme; they can just let their bodies work their magic.

2. Whites are at a disadvantage. Since they're handicapped by bad genes, and therefore by their anatomy and physiology, they will never be able to compete equally with Africans..

Of course, believers in black 'super-genes' haven't been able to explain exactly how Africans have managed to corner the market on superior genetic material. When the Finns dominated the running world in the 1920s and again in the 1970s, no loud voices proclaimed that Finnish runners were genetically superior. Instead we pondered the merits of reindeer milk and called Lasse Viren a potential blood doper. When the Brits dominated middle-distance running in the 1950s and 1980s, there was no talk about brilliant British genetic material. Rather, we heard about British pluck and hard work. And when the Chinese women ran wild in 1993, it was because they were drugged, not because red-hot genetic material had fired up their performances. But now that Africans are running wild, the genetics lessons begin. Somehow, Providence has chosen to bless only African runners with top-quality DNA..

Although beliefs about genetic differences between African and non-African runners are widely held, it's important to remember that these beliefs are opinions - and nothing more. There's simply no scientific evidence to support the idea that African runners are genetically superior to European, North American, Asian, or South American athletes.. Why isn't there any evidence? At present, we don't even know which genes are necessary for topflight performances! Since we don't know which genes are important, it's impossible to measure the relative frequencies of performance-enhancing genes in different groups of athletes.

In addition, the available scientific research suggests that genetic factors are less important than non-genetic factors (including training and lifestyle) in determining performances.. Still, when Mr. Gebrselassie of Ethiopia rips through the 5K in a world-record 12:44 or Mr. Kiptanui from Kenya slashes the 3000-metre steeplechase mark, the familiar refrain begins again: Africans have the most slender upper bodies, the thinnest bones, the most rail-thin calves, the most tent-like lungs and the most reservoir-like, elephantine hearts - all because they have the optimal genetic make-ups.

Continuing to rely on the 'genetic explanation' for African superiority has negative consequences. After Africans win the vast majority of distance medals at the Atlanta Olympics - as they inevitably will - and then return to their continent, anyone saying that they won their hardware because of their genes is giving a huge insult to their untiring work and relentless motivation. And summoning up the hocus-pocus of genetic differences makes the running community less eager to actually learn something useful from the top African runners. You've probably noticed that people aren't exactly beating down the Africans' doors in order to understand how to train, even though the Africans have blown the socks off runners from the rest of the world.

There are just three relevant studies in the scientific literature that have examined physiological differences between Africans and non-Africans, and none of the three actually looked specifically at gene quality. That's no surprise; since, as mentioned, scientists don't actually know which genes code for endurance performance, they can't possibly determine whether Africans have a lockhold on superior genetic material. Instead of looking at actual genetic differences, scientists have made inferences about genes based on the physiological differences which they detect between blacks and whites.

In a study carried out by Claude Bouchard and his group at Laval University in Quebec, 23 black male students and 23 Caucasian male students were compared. The black students hailed from Cameroon, Senegal, Zaire, the Ivory Coast and Burundi (mainly, that is, from the western and central parts of Africa), while the Caucasians were born in Canada and were of French descent. Both the Africans and Caucasians had an average age of 25, weighed about 154 pounds and were about 5'9' tall. All the students were sedentary at the time of the study.. No gene frequencies were measured, but Bouchard found that both groups had the same percentage (about 18 percent) of type IIb muscle fibres - the cells which are critically important for sprinting (so much for the idea that western Africans have muscles uniquely suited for high-speed running!).

There were two key differences in muscle composition between whites and blacks: Caucasians had a higher percentage of type I cells (41 vs. 33 percent), while Africans checked in with more type IIa muscles (49 vs. 42 percent). As you know, type I fibres are great for prolonged, moderate-speed endurance performance, as in an event like the marathon, while IIa cells promote faster running times in shorter events like the 5K.. Although Africans had more IIa cells and fewer type I cells, we can't say that these differences are genetically based. For one thing, studies show that muscle fibre type is not tightly regulated by genes. Also, an individual's muscle-fibre composition can change over time. IIb fibres can probably become IIa cells, and IIa cells may be able to become type I fibres. Thus, it's impossible to say that the blacks' higher frequency of IIa fibres was a genetic thing..

The only other key difference between the Africans and Canadians was that blacks had higher concentrations of 'anaerobic' muscle enzymes, which are chemicals that spur the production of energy during short, intense running, whereas whites showed up with greater levels of 'aerobic' enzymes needed for continuous, endurance exercise. Again, there's no reason to conclude that these physiological differences are caused by genetic differences. The increased anaerobic-enzyme density in blacks might have simply been the result of their higher frequency of IIa cells.. The Laval scientists concluded that 'black individuals are, in terms of skeletal muscle characteristics, well endowed for sport events of short duration'. That's a somewhat shaky conclusion, since blacks and whites had exactly the same concentrations of IIb cells, the ones which are critical for sprinting, although it was true that blacks had higher amounts of anaerobic enzymes. As mentioned, it was impossible to say why the blacks' muscles were more tilted toward IIa fibres and away from type I cells. It might have been genetics, but it might have been the result of lifestyle, too..

In a separate study carried out several years ago, Tim Noakes and his colleagues at the University of Capetown compared elite black vs. elite white South-African runners. Although both groups had similar 5-K times (about 13:45), the blacks were considerably faster in 10-K and half-marathon races. VO2max, running economy, maximal running velocity, training mileage and the percentage of type I muscle cells were exactly the same in the two groups, but there were some differences:

1. blacks ate more calories and carbohydrate per pound of body weight, compared to whites,
2. blacks trained considerably faster than whites,
3. blacks produced less lactate while running at race speeds, and

4. blacks were quite a bit shorter than whites (5′6' vs. 5′11') and weighed less (123 vs. 154 pounds)..

Note that only point four can be firmly pinned to genetics. Body height - although influenced by the environment - is fairly strongly determined by genes, and body weight tends to follow from height. Eating more calories and carbohydrate (point 1) is a lifestyle factor. Running at higher training speeds (point 2) often is part of an overall training philosophy that emphasises intensity rather than volume and is not necessarily coupled with a particular genetic constitution. Producing less lactate while running at high velocities (point 3) might simply be a long-term result of the more intense training carried out by blacks. Overall, Noakes' work provided no solid evidence that blacks were genetically different from whites.

The most revealing study on this topic was carried out by the renowned Swedish exercise physiologist, Bengt Saltin, who compared sedentary adolescent Kenyans, Kenyan high school runners and elite Kenyan runners with top-level Scandinavian runners. Saltin unearthed a number of important facts. First, relatively sedentary adolescent Kenyans had exactly the same aerobic capacities as sedentary Danish teenagers. If the Kenyans were really genetically superior, you would expect them to have higher VO2maxs than their Scandinavian counterparts (unless their 'superhuman' genes only revealed themselves in response to training).

Second, young Kenyan runners trained with astonishing intensity: About 50 to 60 percent of their total mileage was done at heart rates of 90 percent of maximum or higher! This was significantly higher than the Scandinavians' total and is much higher than anything European and American runners do generally. Third, and following directly from point two, Kenyan runners - including the high schoolers - were more economical than the elite Scandinavians and also produced less lactate during high-speed running. This makes sense: one of the best ways to boost economy is to train fast, and the Kenyans have the corner on intense training. Also, fast training boosts the aerobic qualities of fast-twitch, type IIa muscle cells and lowers their lactate output, which probably explains why the Kenyans have lower lactate levels during strenuous running.

Since high lactates are associated with fatigue, that's a very good thing! The fourth finding - a critical one for the discussion of whether the Kenyans have a genetic edge - was that sedentary adolescent Kenyans had VO2max readings of 47 (the same as Scandinavians), very active (but non-training) Kenyan teenagers had VO2maxs of about 62, and seriously training high school Kenyan runners checked in with average VO2maxs of 65 to 68. Senior elite Kenyan runners have had their VO2max levels measured at 75 to 85. This progression in aerobic capacities from the mid-40s to high-70s and low-80s is exactly the same as the one observed in Americans (sedentary American youth have VO2max values in the 40s, while topflight runners like Salazar, Ryun, and Prefontaine were in the high 70s and low- to mid-80s).

The progression in VO2max values is the same in Kenyans as it is in Americans! In addition, as high school Kenyans become elite senior runners, they increase their number of blood vessels per muscle cell and also enhance the concentrations of energy-producing aerobic enzymes inside their muscle cells. Those are natural responses to hard training and aren't necessarily caused by superior genes.

Proponents of the genetic theory often point out that of the more than 35 tribal groups in Kenya, a single tribe - the Kalenjins - has produced most of the great runners (Lelei, Loroupe, Kiptanui, Keino, Kiprotich, Cheromei, Sang, Rono, etc.). The Kalenjins were traditionally a pastoral people who roamed the beautiful Rift Valley of Kenya with their cattle, so one might argue that genes which enhanced the ability to move long distances were 'selected' over evolutionary time. In contrast, members of another large Kenyan tribe, the Luo, have traditionally fished for a living and have produced few top runners.. However, political and social forces inside the country tend to favour the development of Kalenjins at the expense of other tribes.

In spite of this, the recent trend in Kenyan running has been for non-Kalenjins (Ndeti, Kamau, Kinuthia, Masya, Osano, Asiago, Osoro, Karori, etc.) to become more prominent as time goes by, rather than for Kalenjins to increase their dominance. Most notably, the Kikuyu tribe, always a fine source of running talent (five-time world champion John Ngugi is Kikuyu), is beginning to produce more and more excellent runners, even though the Kikuyus have not interbred with Kalenjins and historically were not a nomadic people. In fact, running talent may be fairly equally distributed among Kenya's tribes. In other words, the Kalenjin-genetic hypothesis weakens once you take a closer look at what's really going on. How could so many different groups of non-interbreeding people produce top runners, if genetic factors were really the paramount factor?

If genes aren't responsible, what accounts for the difference between African and non-African running? The African approach to training differs from the American-European method in a number of ways, including intensity (Africans usually train more intensely but with less mileage), the amount of hill training (there's no comparison here; the Africans are almost always working on hills), periodisation (Africans vary their training more - favouring big upswings and then gentle troughs; in fact, many Africans take a month or two away from running while their American and European peers continue to plug away without a break), and diet (Africans eat more carbohydrate, less protein, and less fat).]

Africans also benefit from a decade-long 'base' period - just running back and forth to junior school at moderate speeds - before they take up serious running, while Americans and Europeans tend to simply plunge into competition in more senior school without a prolonged, strength-boosting build-up.. Many of these factors have already been studied in scientific settings. We know that intensity is the most potent producer of fitness, yet American and European runners still preach the merits of high mileage. We know that hill training is better than flat-ground running, yet American and European runners often limit hill work to once a week. We know that the African diet is more conducive to elite performances, yet American and European runners continue to edge toward more protein and fat.

Rather than speculating about superior genes, let's ask world champions like Mr. Tergat and Ms. Tulu what they are doing in January, March, July and September, and throughout the whole year. Chances are good that we'll pick up some useful information from them. Let's face it, there's no evidence that Africans have a lock on the genes needed for world-record running performances. After all, we don't even know what those genes are, and (as the following note explains) most research has suggested that training and lifestyle - not genetic factors - account for more of the variation in athletic performances. So let's give the Africans credit for earning their world-beating performances. And let's learn from them about how to perform at the best-possible level.

Growth of Fitness and Synergy

The concept of fitness occurs extensively in both the complexity and biology fields, but it is rarely spelled out just what is meant by this and what different forms fitness can take. Fitness usually occurs relative to something else and it is this relativity which is important in understanding the concept within complexity thought. This is not quite the same as when we say a person is 'fit' (an isolated evaluation), which assumes an absolute measure or value, but refers instead to a contextual evaluation, a comparative measure.

Synergy in contrast relates to combinational effects, the systemic change in fitness that occurs when parts come together, when they interact. This brings into play a number of possible interactions and coevolutionary processes, and whilst somewhat neglected in complexity experiments (which are often dominated by 'conflict' scenarios) is expected to become of increasing importance as we attempt to evolve systems adequate in complexity to mimic living systems. It is synergy that relates more to absolute fitnesses, looking to maximise the available value of the combinations.

Ultimately the term fitness has no single meaning, and in biology is often used rather tautologically - what exists must be fit (adaptive) by definition. This sense assumes that fitness relates only to survival and/or reproduction and makes no valid claim to optimisation. A relative or differential fitness of this type is contextual, it has meaning only by comparison with the other options or variants available at that particular time and location.

In complexity thought we are often concerned more with what is the best that can be achieved (optimization), and in searching state space for all possible solutions, rather than just those that currently exist (as in biology). Additionally, values other than survival/reproduction can be important (e.g. economic, energetic, artistic, scientific) and thus we can extend the fitness idea to multiple values, giving a overall 'quality of life' performance measure for any complex task. In many treatments however the traditional concept of reproduction is retained and the reproduction rate or survival is made proportional, in some way, to the fitness function employed, in determining the evolutionary dynamics of the system.

Static Fitness

To investigate fitness more deeply, let us first consider a landscape, comprising hills and valleys. Over our lifetime it can be said to be static, it doesn't change. If we decide (arbitrarily) to make height our measure of fitness then we can see that if we move about the landscape then we can attempt to maximise this fitness, to climb the highest hill. This idea is central to Genetic Algorithms, which mutate and crossover genes to move the organism around a state space landscape, trying to find the highest (i.e. most fit) point. We can regard such a two dimensional landscape as the x and y co-ordinates of two continuously variable genes, but typically many genes are involved and thus we need a multidimensional landscape - a difficult to visualise hypercube.

Note that the measure (height) was arbitrary, thus we can choose any measure to maximise, and this depends critically upon the problem we wish to solve. Typically all we need to be able to do is to calculate a fitness for every combination of variables, we can then use GAs as a search technique to locate the optimum solution to our problem (or perhaps more typically one solution from many). It is important to note that a poor choice of fitness measure will generate an invalid initial landscape and thus invalid solutions to the problem (e.g. height may be quite appropriate for an mountaineer but poor for someone trying to get out of a freezing wind !).

Dynamic Fitness

Now let us consider instead seawater, here the wave peaks are not static they change position with time. Using the same height criterion we can see that our fitness will vary in time, even if we do nothing, our 'landscape' changes regardless of our behaviour. This scenario applies to cyclic weather effects in nature, as well as to longer term environmental changes. An animal or plant will experience different fitnesses depending upon the climate being experienced (and location, i.e. tropical forest, temperate grasslands, arctic waste), so fitness is always environmentally relative and is a function both of the changing landscape and the organism variables. Usually we keep one of these constant, maximising individual fitness for a given landscape or seeing how, say, a cooling landscape affects a particular individual optimum.

It is this aspect of fitness that is often treated in evolutionary biology, when we claim that the organism evolves to fit its landscape. Bear in mind that several behaviours (e.g. hibernation, migration, woolly jumpers) can compensate for environmental changes of this sort, so fitness can be said to relate to how well the organism can compensate for adverse conditions or exploit good ones. This tracking of a moving landscape relates to Neural Networks, where the system tries to recognise and adapt to changing inputs. This also shows that rather than evolving body features over multiple generations, lifetime learning is also a way of improving fitness - a dynamic correlation between short term landscape variation and behaviour.

Coevolutionary Fitness

In most of nature however there is not just one organism on the landscape, there are many, and they affect each other (e.g. predator and prey). In this case the fitness values for any behaviour depends not only on our own action but upon those of our neighbours - we affect each other's decisions. For example if the prey moves North then that becomes the 'fit' direction for the predator - the fitness peak is where the prey is. Note here that the opposite is true for the prey - its fitness peak is where the predator is not ! This is not always the case as we see later in the synergy discussion.

The dynamic nature of such interactions means that the fitness landscape of every organism distorts somewhat following the actions of all those other organisms with which it interacts. This is coevolution in action, sometimes called the 'Red Queen' effect or an 'arms race' on the assumption that coevolution means competition - two adaptations oppose each other and cancel, we "run on the spot". This form of interaction however is common in Artificial Life studies (as well as in ecologies) and means that we cannot impose an external global fitness measure on the system, fitnesses must arise in a dynamic internal way as the system evolves (taking into account all interactional effects).

Epistasis and Multioptimisation

So far we have assumed that fitnesses for organisms were single values, i.e. that the effects of the genes could be summed to give a specific phenotype value such that all genetic combinations would be different. That is rarely the case. Genes affect each other, the effect of one depends upon the values of others, giving a nonlinear phenotype function. This effect, called epistasis, means that we often need to compromise between genetic values. This means, crucially, that the maximum practical fitness may be much less than a derived theoretical one which assumes each gene can be independently optimised (reductionist style).

Several techniques have been developed to calculate fitnesses for such combinations of incompatible values (e.g. multioptimisation, schemas). When this is done we often find that many combinations give the same compromise fitness, thus there may be no single 'global optimum' solution available if we take everything into account. The difficulty of dealing with these more realistic multidimensional cases is what makes fitness such a difficult concept in practice, especially where multiple individual values combine with multiple organisms in a complex environmental ecology (e.g. Kauffman's NKCS model).

Landscape Structure

When we study how the structure of the fitness landscape varies with epistasis K (once again assuming a static landscape for simplicity here) we find three styles:

a) No Epistasis - all variables independent (K=0) These static landscapes have a single hill, with a global maximum that can be reached by single mutations at a time. The fittest organisms cluster around the peak as a single optimised population, but drift will prevent the genotype becoming completely homogeneous.

b) Maximum Epistasis - all variables affect each other (K=N) These are maximally disorganised landscapes (chaotic) with multiple low peaks. Evolution quickly finds a local optimum (one peak at random) but cannot easily escape that niche. Multiple separate populations can coexist, distributed across the landscape.

c) Optimum Epistasis - on average only a few dependencies (K=2 or so) These are correlated landscapes where peaks cluster together, giving linked populations (rather like islands connected by bridges) of good compromise fitnesses.

If we again introduce the dynamics of coevolution we find that the organisms mutually evolve in a way that maximises their combined fitnesses (or at least achieves a stable balance, called an Evolutionary Stable Strategy or ESS). This position, called the 'edge of chaos', corresponds to optimised epistasis since mutations have tried different combinations (higher and lower connectivity) and the fittest has prevailed.

Survival and Values

Once we allow for values other than reproduction then fitness becomes a multi-dimensional spatial and temporal measure, instead of just a multi-generational temporal one. Higher organisms at least, unlike bacteria, generally do not choose to reproduce as fast as possible, i.e. many creatures spend very little of their time doing anything 'useful' in this sense... The set of choices available to organisms expands once they become more complex and aware. We need to consider then just what animals (and humans) are valuing, what is being 'selected' in context .

If not mainly reproductive ability then what ? Little attention has been given to this aspect of life processes, but taking humans as an example many other interests are evident. How are these affected by fitness concepts and how do they relate to the traditional view of competitive exclusion (the idea that the fastest reproducing 'winner' strain will take all) ? Here we need to go somewhat beyond the 'Nature, red in tooth and claw' image so close to the neo-Darwinist heartland.

Synergy

The idea that organisms do not compete destructively to reproduce (if predators ate all the available prey they would then starve and go extinct !) but must ultimately achieve a balance beneficial to all (i.e. somehow 'husband' their resources) brings us to synergy. This says that parts combined have different effects than the parts alone (i.e. the whole is not equal to the sum of the parts) and extends epistasis to the whole system. We already know that one organism can have a negative effect on another (e.g. the predator on prey) but it is often forgotten in our competitive society that this is a minor aspect of nature, cooperative effects are far more common, and are fitter in absolute terms.

These include the emergence effects common to complexity thinking (molecules making cells, cells making organisms, organisms making societies) but also much more. A group of people can achieve what a single one cannot (e.g. building a Cathedral), division of labour increases efficiency and thus group fitness. Symbiosis between fungi and plants is essential for survival in 90% of species, eukaryotic cells are forms of symbiosis, humans also cannot survive without bacterial symbionts. At all levels of nature advantages arise from associations between organisms and this should be true also in our artificial systems.

Evolution Strategies

Given that interactions can be both positive and negative in fitness terms, what forms of fitness effects can we expect to see ? These can be divided into many forms but classify into 4 types:

Forms of Interaction

— Mutually beneficial - $F(a)+F(b) < F(a+b)$ e.g. cleaner fish, lichen (symbiosis)

— Beneficial for one, neutral for rest - $F(a)+F(b) \rightarrow (1+x)F(a)+F(b)$ e.g. shelter under a tree (commensalism)

— Beneficial for one, destructive for rest - $F(a)+F(b) \rightarrow (1+x)F(a)+(1-y)F(b)$ e.g. predator/prey, exploitation (parasitism)

— Mutually destructive - F(a)+F(b) > F(a+b) e.g. war, fighting, conflict (competition)

The first two forms enhance absolute 'system' fitness overall (positive-sum), the last two decrease it in the long term (negative-sum).

Forms of Synergy [from Corning]

— Linear Effects - size advantages due to grouping together, e.g. army power

— Threshold Phenomena - overcoming a barrier, e.g. lifting a large rock

— Phase Transitions - e.g. oxygenation of the primordial atmosphere

— Emergent Phenomena - e.g. alloys with different properties to the constituents

— Functional Complementaries - complementary parts, e.g. Velcro

— Augmentation & Facilitation - e.g. catalysts

— Environmental Conditioning - e.g. huddling together to save warmth

— Risk & Cost Sharing - e.g. flocking, collective foraging

— Information Sharing - gaining knowledge without trial and error

— Society - division of labour, mutual help

— Functional Convergencies - fortuitous by-products of selfish actions, e.g. market prices

Given this collection of mutually beneficial ways to improve our fitness, we must say that the emphasis on 'competition' seen throughout both complex system and biological evolutionary studies is strange. Given that we wish to build complex systems (or in biology explain those that exist), it seems clear that mechanisms that build up complexity (positive-sum synergies) are to be preferred to those that destroy (negative-sum dysergies).

Competitive Losses

Having stressed the fitness benefits of synergistic ideas, we need to indicate why competition is negative-sum, especially as such behaviours are so evident in our societies. What does competition achieve ? In biology survival relates to differential fitness, not to absolute fitness, thus competition can improve relative survival (biologically, a quantitative change in genotype frequency) - presuming a choice must be made between you and me, and that is a critical point.

In most scenarios several other options are available, opportunities for 'value add', for increasing the fitness of both parties (ecologically, a qualitative change in phenotype properties). These relate to untried options in state space, and allow for growth and innovation. Failure to consider these wider aspects of fitness (the coevolutionary interplay between coding/replicator and expression/interactor spaces, along with environmentally mediated developmental processes) - due to a blinkered and dogmatic idea of what is 'fit', can lead to many unforeseen and hidden losses, e.g. in business areas:

— Retaliation - coevolution means my nastiness will be returned, hurting me

— Destruction - mutual negation of advantage (Red Queen) is a fitness loss

— Waste - many resources are needed to pursue the competitive scenario

— Lost Opportunities - enemies never try to cooperate, even when obviously beneficial

— Deceit Costs - lack of trust means effort wasted in monitoring/verification

— Monopoly Costs - eliminating the competition itself imposes prevention costs

Competition is often said to drive innovations (necessity being the mother of invention), but it seems clear that such innovations must be limited to the level of the competitive entity, growth beyond that level (i.e. emergence) can only logically come from the non-destructive interaction of units. Competition between population members by itself isn't adequate to lead towards a synthesis of new constructs since no incentive exists towards cooperative interactions. Yet, in all realms, cooperative behaviour has not gone extinct. Furthermore in most areas, of the biological realm as well as in social ones, it is the crucial property which has led to evolutionary increases in complexity.

Modular Fitness

The emphasis on conflict (either/or) within fitness studies obscures the fact that nature operates extensively at a modular level, by the use of cooperative components that together (both) create some added functionality. In other words, the population of different phenotypes do not compete with each other but evolve to give a better collective fitness by mutualism effects than would be possible for any of them as individuals. Studies on the fitness effects of such synergies (compositional evolution) are rare and may perhaps best be seen in work in Game Theory, where in scenarios like the 'Iterated Prisoners Dilemma' ongoing cooperation can be shown to be fitter than selfish behaviours, but even here studies are limited to a single level of simplified behaviours.

It is hard however to relate this one-dimensional fitness to the synergistic benefits of multi-organism interactions, using multiple values or functions. In part this reflects the peremptory avoidance of group selection in genetics, and the corresponding neglect of higher level effects elsewhere in biology. All levels however are equally important to a complexity view and an overall fitness evaluation must consider them. Some progress in recognising the importance of modularity as a way of improving absolute fitness and generating complexity is now evident, but much work needs to be done before such an approach is put on a solid footing.

This also needs to take into account how such synergistic effects completely change the fitness criteria for survival itself, thus differential fitness in human society is very different than it was before the advent of cooperative society - neither competition by exploitation nor by interference need play any part in our future evolution.

Functional Integration

When different organisms or individuals come together as a group, i.e. they cooperate, then it becomes possible for them to specialise. The efficiency of this mode has been clear ever since Adam Smith's 'pin' example in "The Wealth of Nations", and of course it forms the basis of all modern 'division-of-labour' business practices. It is often not recognised however that not only does the same process apply to the organization of societies, but that once again nature did it first. Ecosystems are largely maintained by such synergic (niche oriented) processes, but there is a problem.

In modular organisations there is sufficient local knowledge to detect the cheaters, and thus to impose costs upon them sufficient to limit their spread. In other words interactions are not random, but selected, historical behaviour constrains future interactions, based upon a form of trust. Socially cooperating organisms ostracise exploitative behaviour, they can detect the untrustworthy (an evolved instinctive trait).

In a large global society there are however many places to hide, and this historical knowledge can be lost, cheaters can then thrive - a problem we see throughout the modern human world. In synergic terms, homogeneity is fitness reducing, heterogeneous modularity (a set of niched and localised cooperating phenotypes) is potentially superior - if this invasion problem can be overcome, an area still very much under researched (even in game theory).

Multi-Level Selection

The key to such containment may lie in multi-level selection. This is the idea that group effects force a 'downward causation' selection on the lower level individuals, e.g. human (higher level) social laws incarcerate criminals (individual cheaters). It is beginning to be realised that these effects are ubiquitous, in natural as well as in cultural evolution (e.g. in multicellular modifiers). This form of 'group selection' does not actually need competition between groups (as usually thought) but is self-contained, an 'internal selection' or self-organization operates instead, the social or modular group itself acts as an adaptive environment for the individuals contained within it.

Thus the behaviours of other individuals within the group can constrain deviants by coevolutionary processes. This implies that fitnesses vary with the composition of the group, which acts as another level of selective relevance upon the evolution of varying structures (e.g. frequency-dependent selection). A group-dependent competitive evolution of this sort is sometimes called a 'structured-deme model'. These concepts can be easily generalised to incorporate multiple species, i.e. ecological multilevel evolution.

Rather than thinking of groups as isolated and competing however we must recognise the possibilities of dynamic migration both into and out of each group, in this way the different behaviours and values that have evolved in the separate groups can mix, i.e. a cultural exchange is made possible. By limiting in some way such dispersal between groups however we act to freeze their dynamics (a static move, allowing equilibrium to develop, e.g. a totalitarian closed society), whilst by opening them up to free movement we act to disrupt their local dynamics (a chaotic move, constantly perturbing with 'new blood', e.g. a society fully open and keen to embrace the latest fads). The balance between these effects, i.e. a society or ecology that can maintain its traditions yet also adapt, is epitomised by the term 'edge of chaos'.